e. ranuc

D1177848

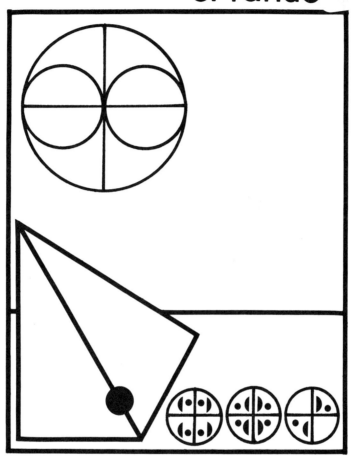

seeing shapes

CREATIVE PUBLICATIONS, INC.   PALO ALTO, CALIFORNIA

THE AUTHOR AND PUBLISHER HEREBY GRANT
PERMISSION TO TEACHERS TO REPRODUCE UP
TO 50 COPIES OF ANY PART OF THIS BOOK
FOR USE IN THE CLASSROOM!

Copyright 1973 Creative Publications, Inc.
P. O. Box 10328
Palo Alto, California 94303

ISBN:0-88488-038-9

1.576.7

INTRODUCTION

In the teaching of mathematics during the last twenty years there has been an emphasis on abstraction. This emphasis on abstraction has, unfortunately, been accompanied all too often by a lack of emphasis on the concrete. One area which has suffered is that of space perception and the understanding of spatial relationships.

Seeing Shapes provides exercises which strengthen the space perception abilities of students. *Abilities,* plural, because these perceptual factors are a complex structure of many components.

The materials are suited for use from Grades 7 to the junior college level. There is, apparently very little relation between the age of a student and his ability to comprehend spatial relationships. Consequently, young people will sometimes handle spatial phenomena better than older students.

Emphasis throughout Seeing Shapes is on discovery. We are not concerned with precision in drawing. Drawing is merely one method by which students can discover spatial relationships. We seek to provoke imaginative thinking through the stimuli of imaginative visual materials.

TABLE OF CONTENTS

PART I

ORTHOGRAPHIC AND ISOMETRIC DRAWINGS

Everyone should have some basic understanding of descriptive drawing. Drawings, after all, are as important to the communication of ideas as words. In many cases a simple drawing can convey information much more clearly than any amount of verbal communication either spoken or written.

ORTHOGRAPHIC DRAWINGS

One of the most useful types of pictorial communication is called *orthographic drawing* or *orthographic projection.* The literal meaning of orthographic is perpendicular. In this case the literal meaning is quite descriptive, inasmuch as orthographic projections are drawings based on three perpendicular views of an object as shown in Figure 1. The illustration also shows what is meant by the term projection. As you can see, the three views can be thought of as projections onto planes perpendicular to three lines of sight. Here too is an example of a drawing communicating information much more clearly than words. Orthographic drawings are used extensively in the fields of engineering, design and architecture because they can clearly and accurately describe complex forms. They are also part of an international language. Technicians anywhere in the world can "read" orthographic drawings because they have become standardized forms of pictorial communication.

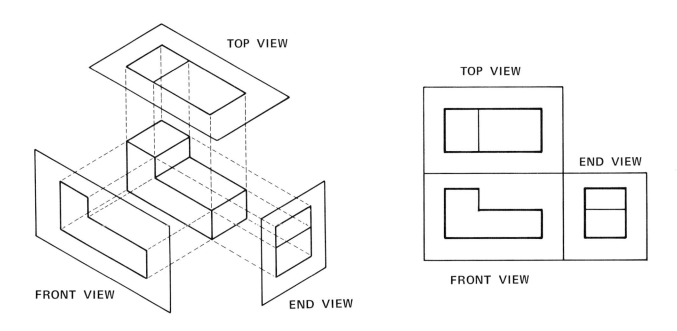

FIGURE 1   ORTHOGRAPHIC PROJECTION

7

ISOMETRIC DRAWINGS

Another standard form of pictorial communication is the *isometric* drawing. The isometric drawing is an attempt to portray three dimensional shapes on a two dimensional page. As can be seen in Figure 2 it is quite successful. The word isometric means equal measure and refers to the equal angles used in the drawing. An isometric drawing starts with one or two sets of three rays representing perpendicular edges of a three dimensional object. The isometric cube in Figure 3 indicates these sets of rays and gives the standard angles. Note that rays B,C,D and E represent horizontal edges and ray A represents a vertical edge. On the real cube of course, these edges would be at 90° to one another. Using the conventional 60° and 120° angles allows us to portray the cube in a way that resembles a perspective view with a minimum of distortion and without the complexities of the converging lines found in perspective drawings.

FIGURE 2   ISOMETRIC DRAWING

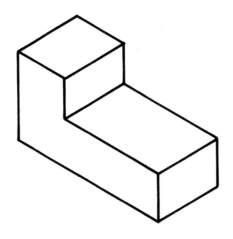

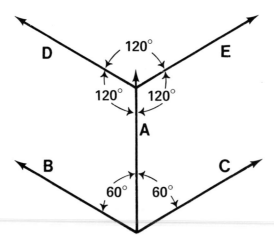

FIGURE 3   ANGLES OF ISOMETRIC DRAWING

COMPARING ORTHOGRAPHIC AND ISOMETRIC DRAWINGS

In Figure 1 we saw how orthographic projections were developed from a three dimensional object. In that diagram an isometric drawing of the object was used to represent the three dimensional object. It helped to show that the orthographic drawing is a projection of three views of the object onto planes. In fact the isometric drawing shows the same three views as the orthographic drawing; we should, therefore, be able to look at an orthographic drawing and construct the isometric drawing and vice versa. Figure 4 illustrated three examples of sets of isometric and orthographic drawings of the same object. The faces have been given letter designations to help identify them in the various views.

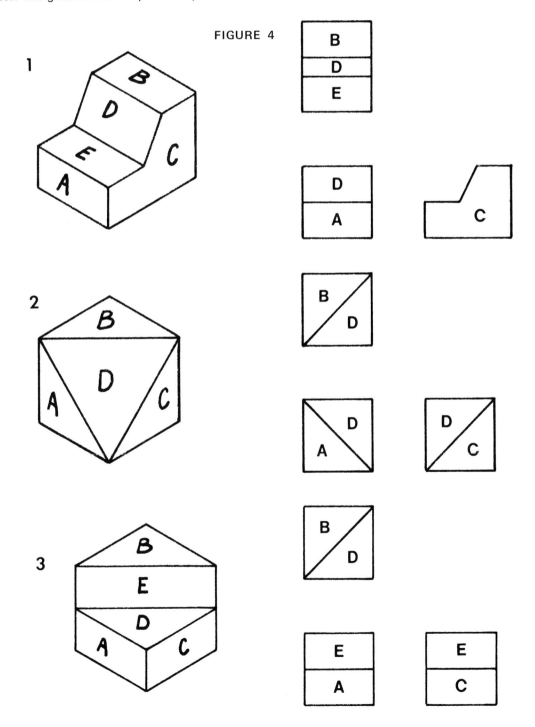

FIGURE 4

9

HIDDEN LINES

When viewed from a certain direction, an edge or part of an edge of an object may be hidden from view. When this is the case in an orthographic projection the hidden edge is shown as a dotted line as shown in Figure 5. If a hidden line and a visible line coincide, the line is shown as solid as seen in Figure 6.

FIGURE 5

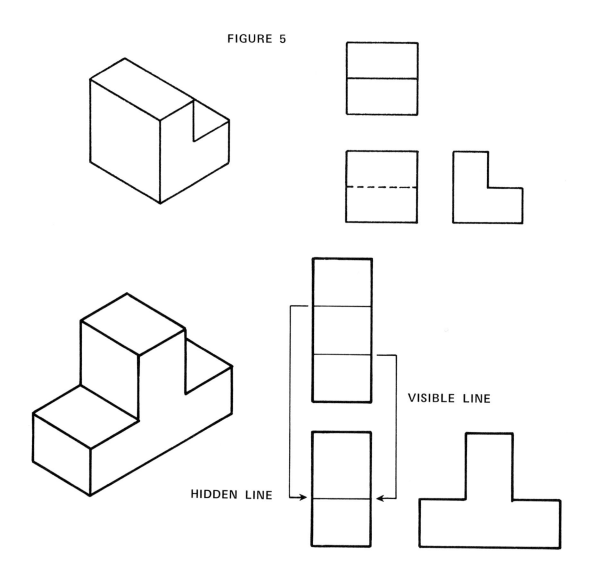

FIGURE 6   HIDDEN AND VISIBLE LINES

EXERCISES

The exercises in this chapter require an understanding of orthographic and isometric projections and their relationship. They give excellent practice in "reading" both kinds of drawings and visualizing three dimensional objects as described by two dimensional representations. Both activities strengthen the general ability of the student to visualize.

EXERCISE 1-A

The object of the exercises in this section is to select the one set of orthographic projections from the four in each row that describes the same object as the isometric drawing on the left.

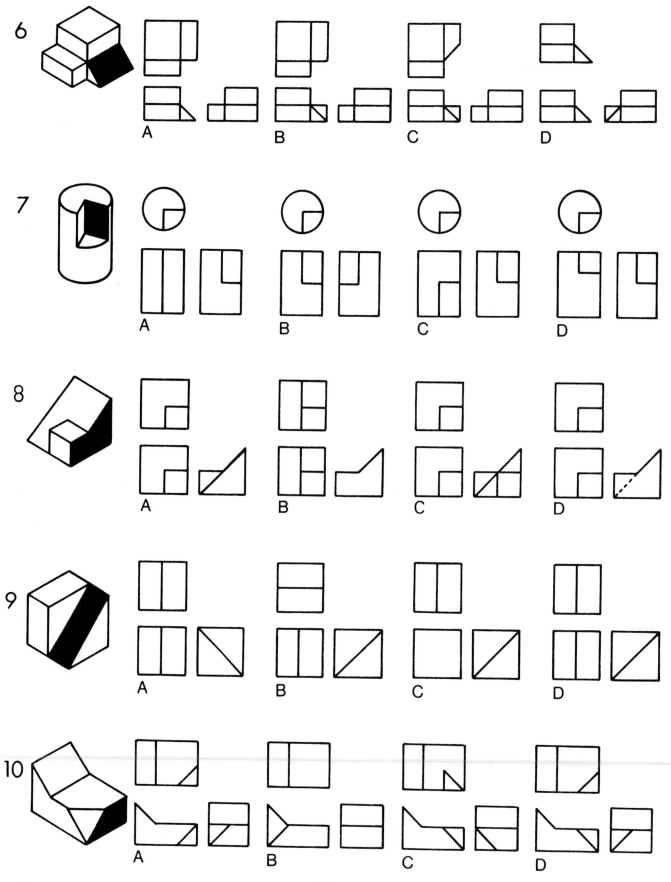

6   A   B   C   D

7   A   B   C   D

8   A   B   C   D

9   A   B   C   D

10   A   B   C   D

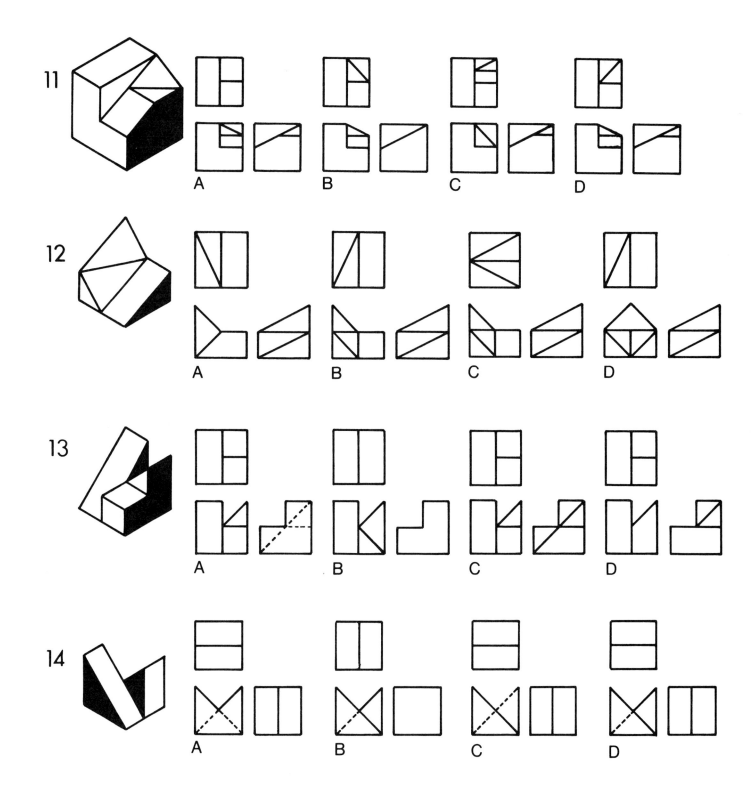

11

A B C D

12

A B C D

13

A B C D

14

A B C D

EXERCISE 1-B

Draw the orthographic projections of the objects shown in the following isometric drawings.

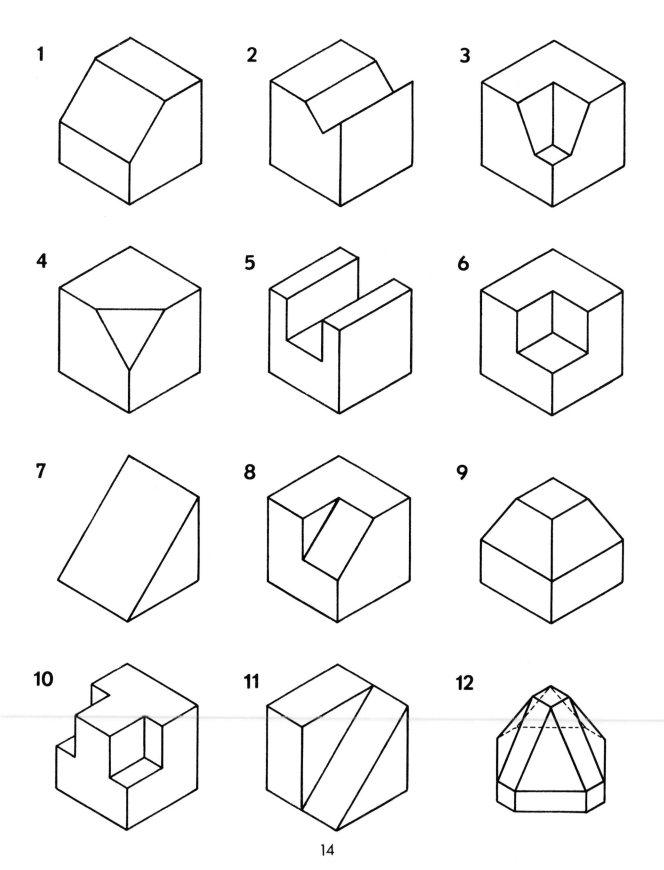

1
2
3
4
5
6
7
8
9
10
11
12

13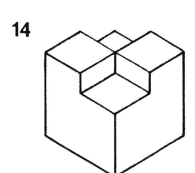

14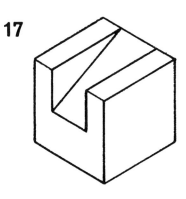

15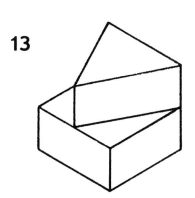

16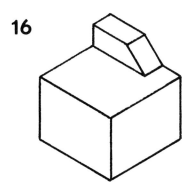

17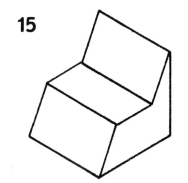

18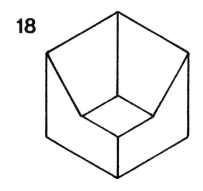

19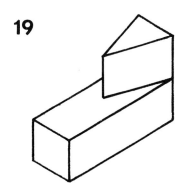

EXERCISE 1-C
Draw the isometric drawings of the objects shown in the following orthographic projections.

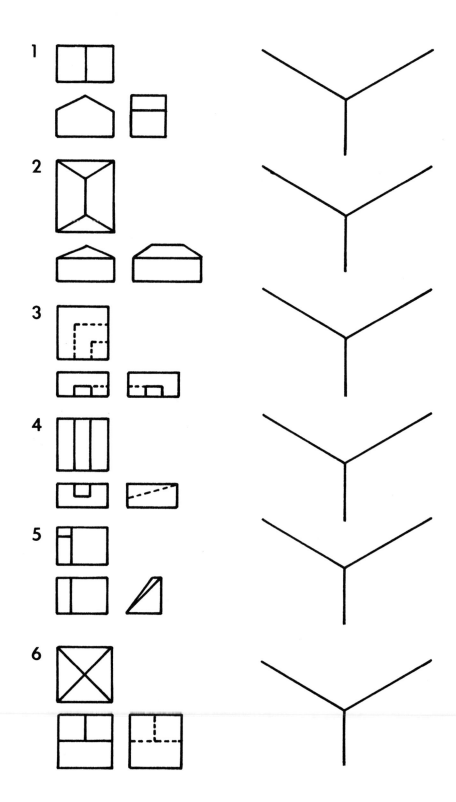

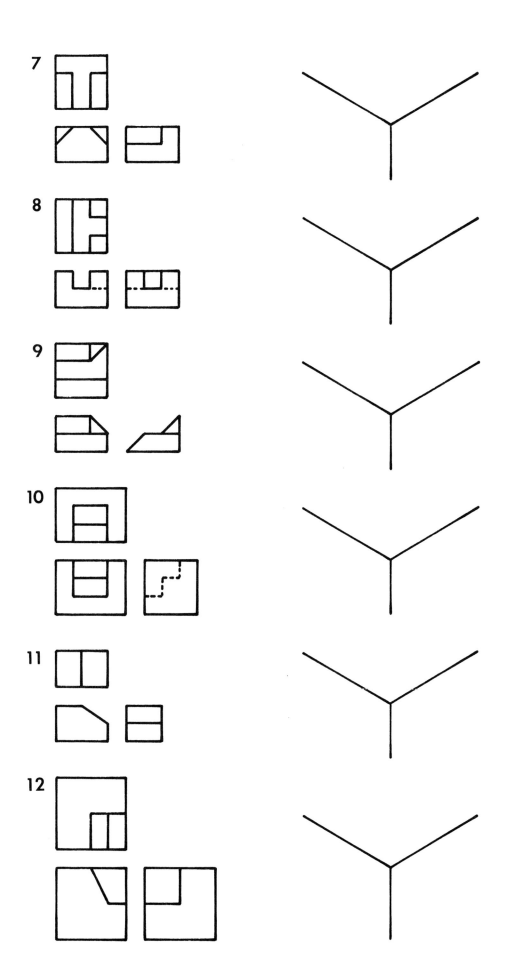

PART II

PAPER FOLDING AND CUTTING

Another group of activities that can help students develop their visualization of spatial relationships are those involving paper folding. In the following exercises it is not necessary to actually fold, perforate or cut the paper. You should visualize what happens without actually folding, cutting or perforating the paper.

EXERCISE 2-A

In these exercises you are to visualize a rectangular sheet of paper folded in half and then folded in half again as shown in Figure 1. While it is folded this way imagine holes of various shapes and location cut through all the layers (see Figure 2). After this is done imagine the sheet of paper unfolded and spread out again as shown in Figure 2. The lines dividing the unfolded sheet represent the creases of the folding. The challenge, then, is to select from four alternatives in each row the one which represents the correct pattern of holes based on the folded sheet at the left of each row.

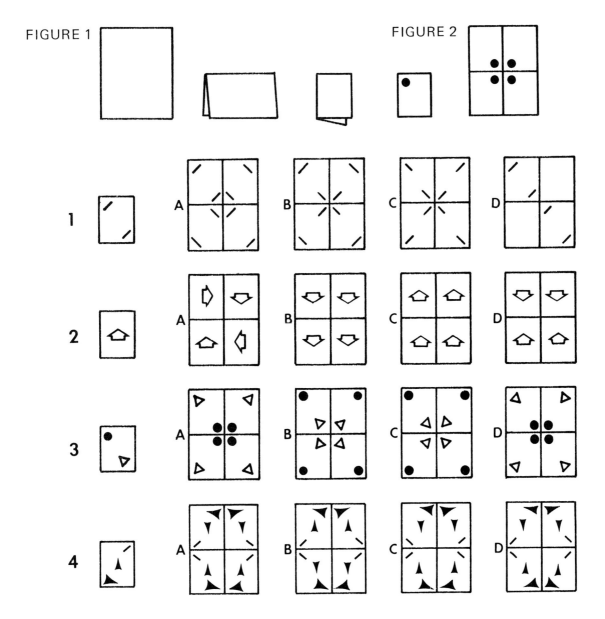

5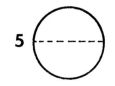

A 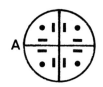 B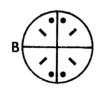

C   D

6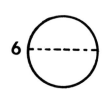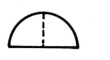

A  B

C   D

7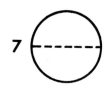

A B

C   D

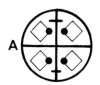

20

EXERCISE 2-B

In these exercises the paper is first folded in half the long way and then in thirds as shown in Figure 1. While it is folded this way, imagine holes of various shape and location cut through all the layers. After this is done imagine the sheet of paper unfolded and spread out again as shown in Figure 2. The lines dividing the unfolded sheet represent the creases of the folding. The challenge, then, is to select from four alternatives in each row the one which represents the correct pattern of holes based on the folded sheet at the left of each row.

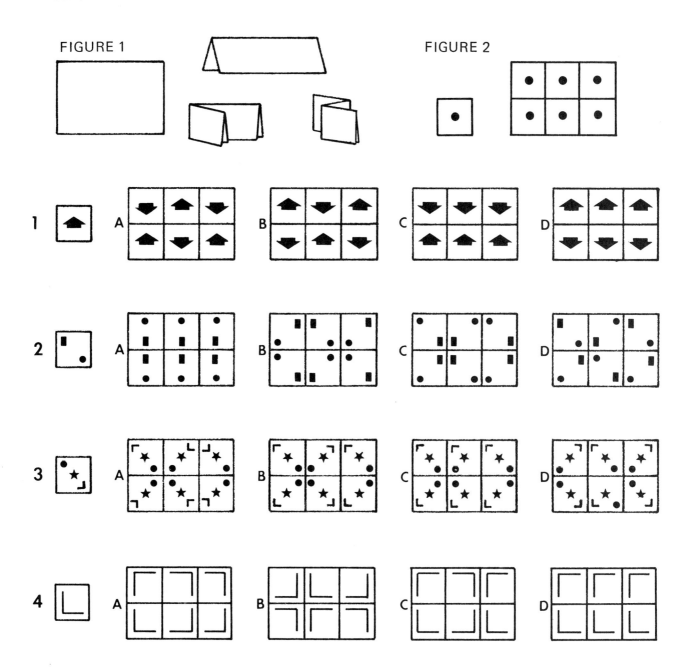

21

EXERCISE 2-C

In this series of exercises a variety of folds are used. The fold used is shown above each row. The object is to select the pattern that would result if the paper were folded and perforated as indicated in the figure at the left of each row and then unfolded. Use your imagination—don't actually fold or cut the paper.

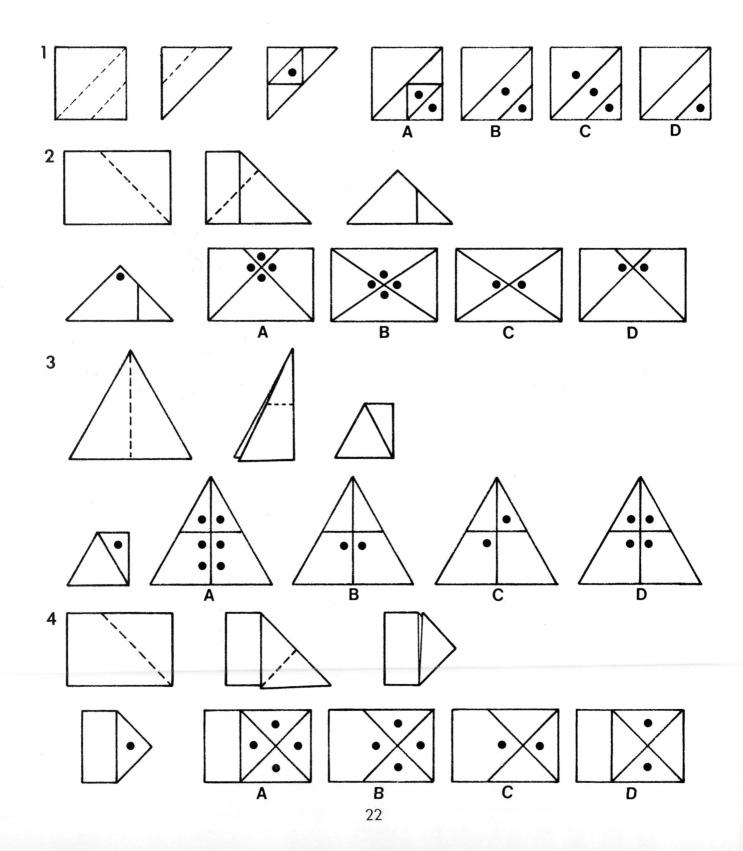

22

EXERCISE 2-D

In this section imagine that the paper is folded and cut along each of the indicated lines. Match each of these with the patterns from A to J. Solid lines indicate cuts. Dotted lines indicate creases. Number 1, for example, is paired with I. In like manner, pair equilateral triangles 11-20 with patterns K to T.

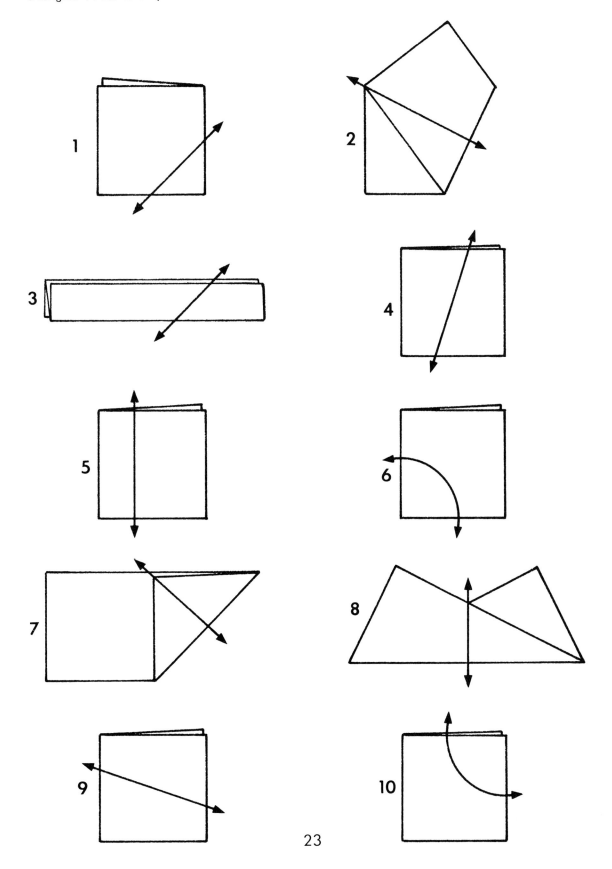

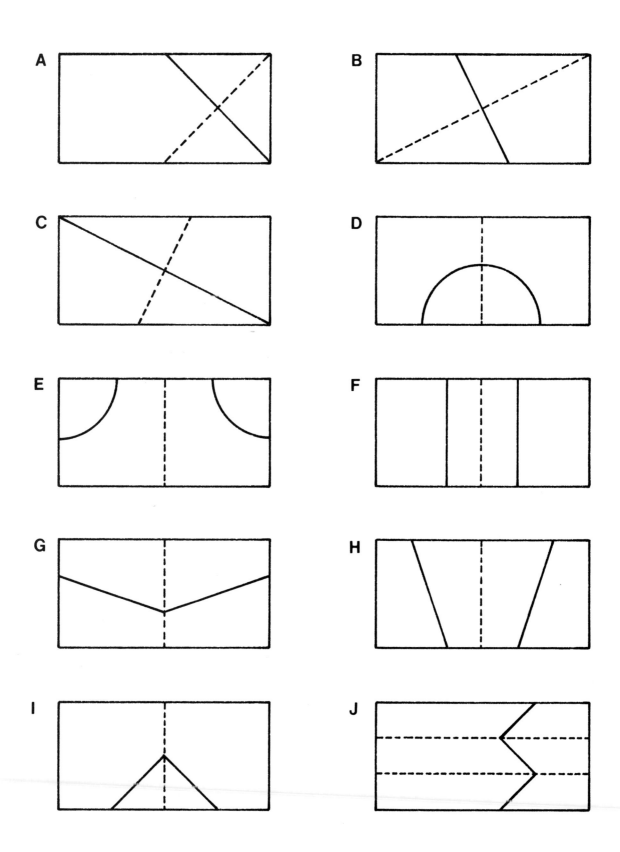

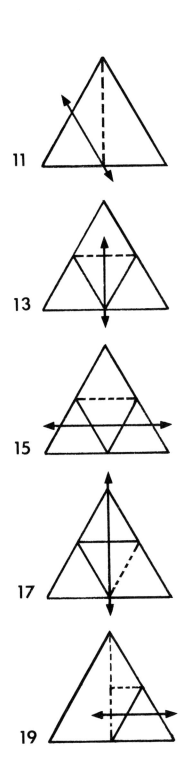

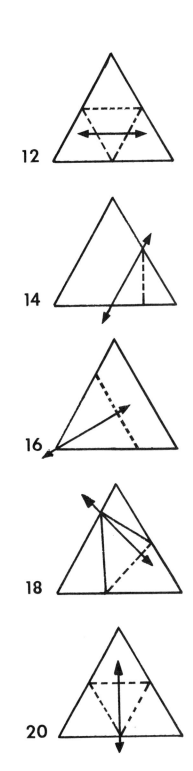

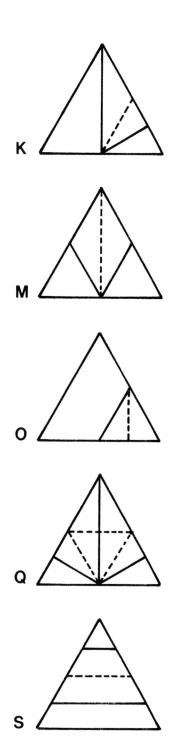

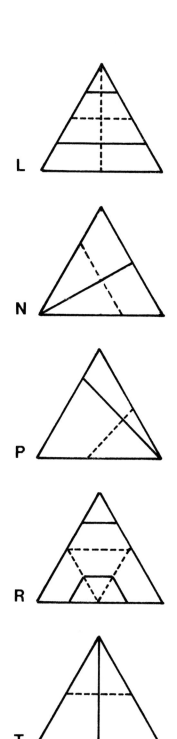

EXERCISE 2-E

The rectangle in the drawing is folded so that corner 2 and corner 1 are brought together. Then another fold is made so that corner 3 meets corner 4. The result is shown in the last diagram is the sequence. See whether or not you can answer these questions without actually folding the rectangle:

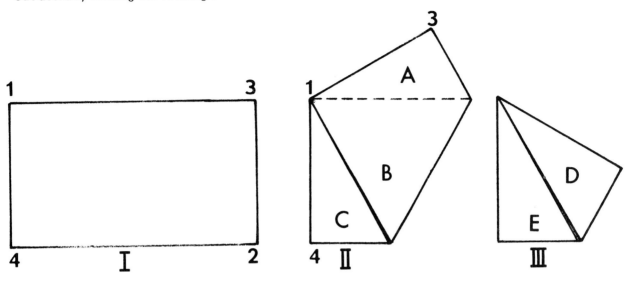

1. How many thicknesses of paper will you find at A?

2. How many thicknesses of paper will you find at B?

3. How many thicknesses of paper will you find at C?

4. How many thicknesses of paper will you find at D?

5. How many thicknesses of paper will you find at E?

6. What will the original rectangle look like when the folded paper is reopened?

EXERCISE 2-F

The figures in this section folded as illustrated in Figure 1. The dark areas indicate sections that have been cut out. They go through all the layers that they overlap. The object is to match these numbered figures with the appropriate lettered diagram on the following page which represents the unfolded layout.

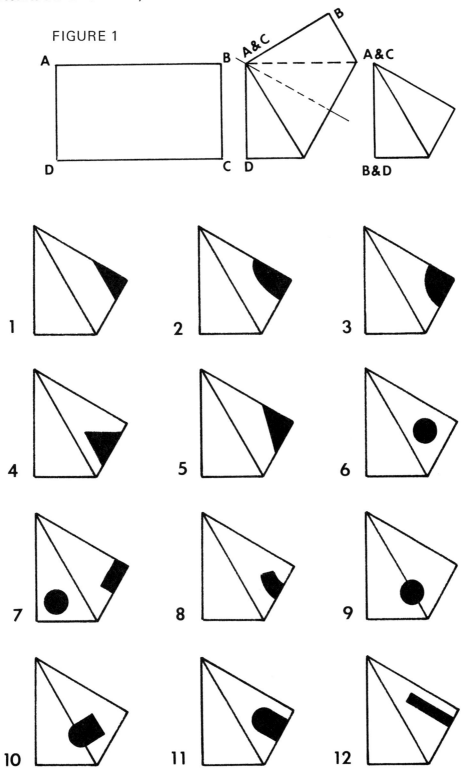

FIGURE 1

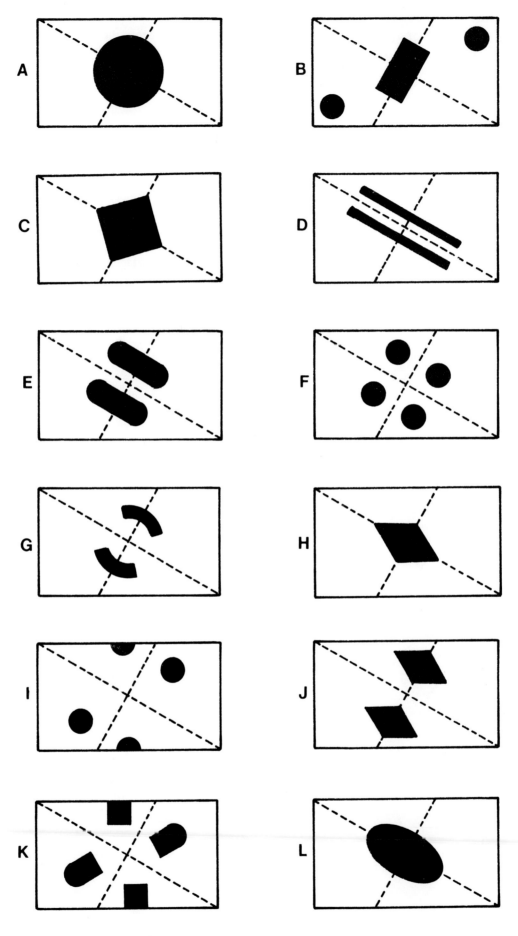

EXERCISE 2-G

In this exercise you start with a hexagonal piece of paper. Imagine that it is folded along the dotted lines and then perforated as indicated by the black circles. Match the numbered items on this page with the lettered items on the next page.

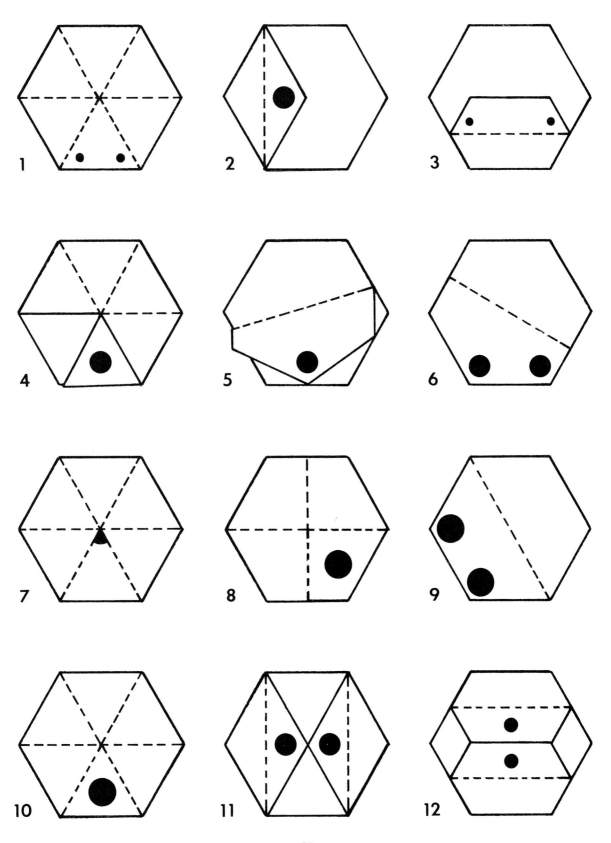

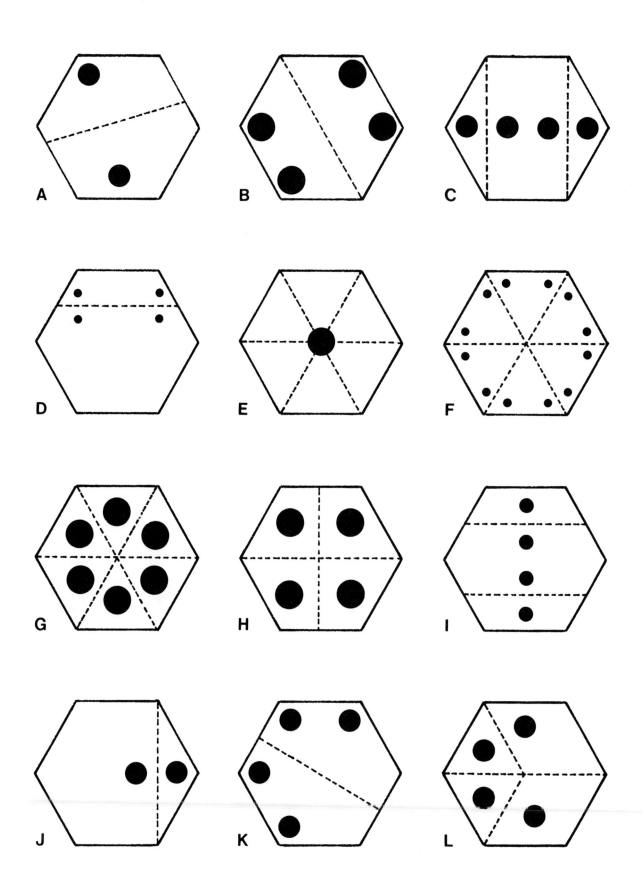

EXERCISE 2-H

The figures on the left of each row in this section represent the layout of an unfolded box with designs on several panels. To the right are four isometric drawings of boxes with designs on several faces. The object is to select the isometric drawing that matches the layout.

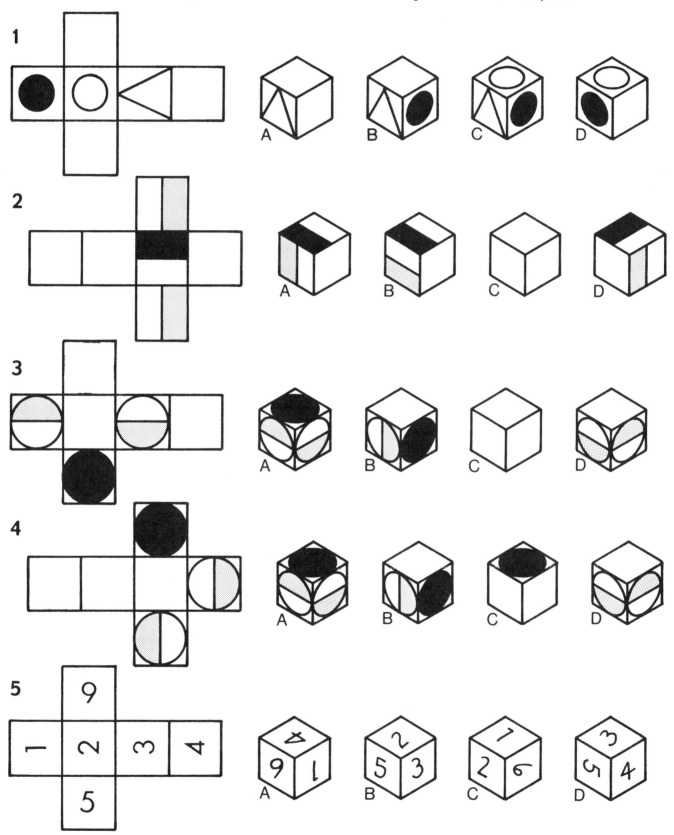

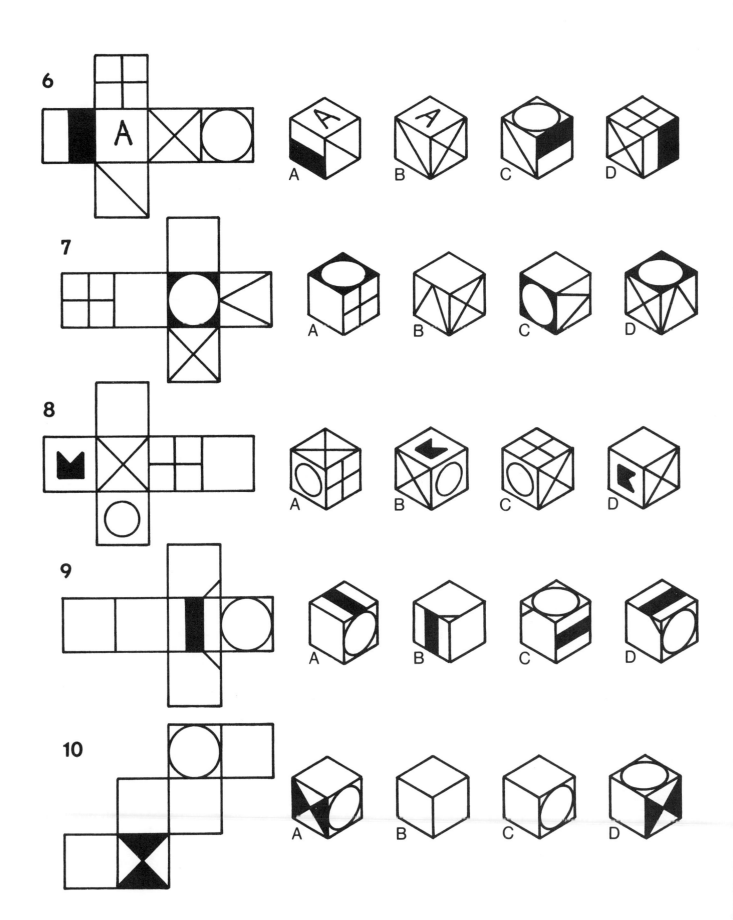

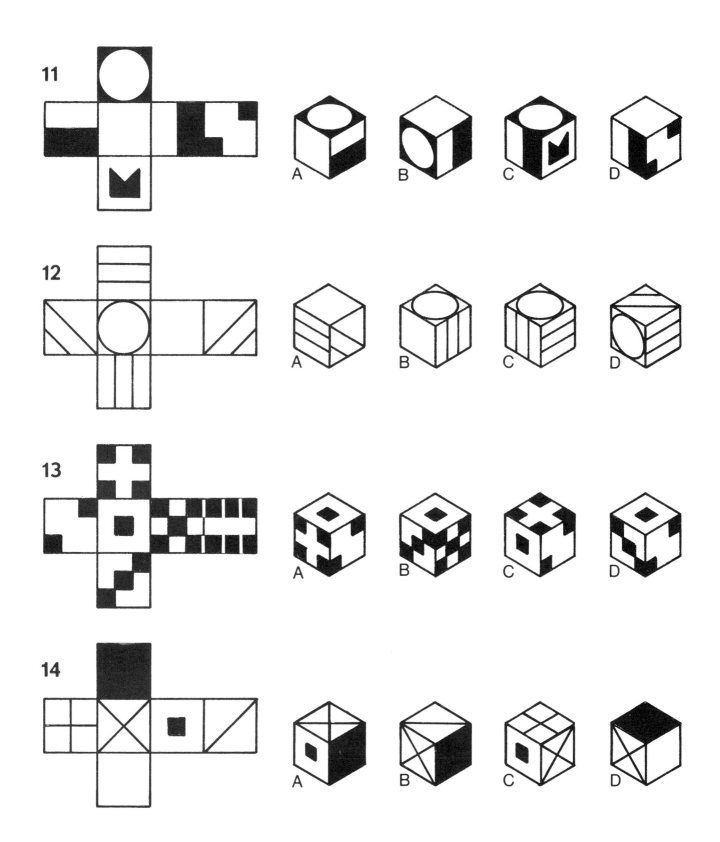

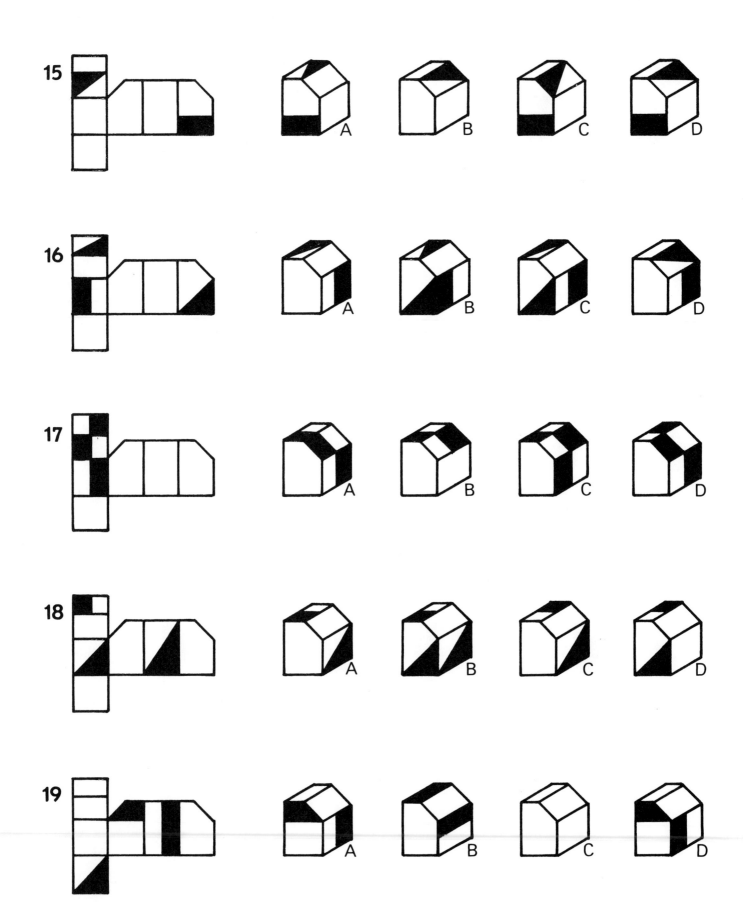

20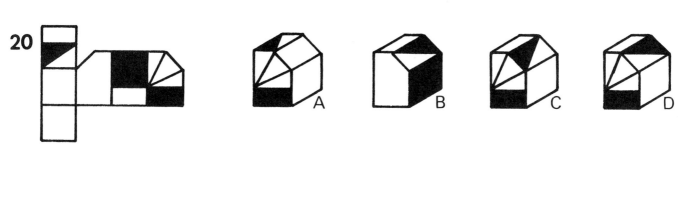

21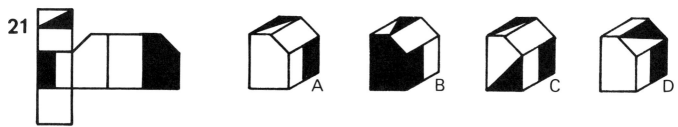

22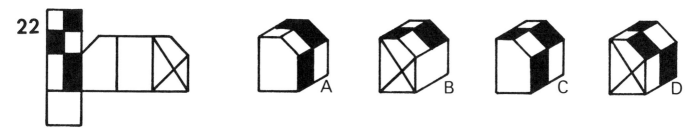

23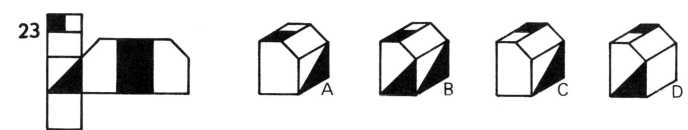

24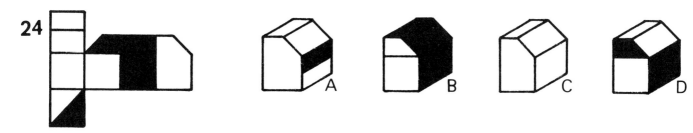

EXERCISE 2-1

In this section, patterns or layouts for various shaped solids are shown. Each edge has a two letter designation. The object is to list those edges which will be joined together when the layout is folded into the solid. Figure 1 shows a cube as an example.

FIGURE 1

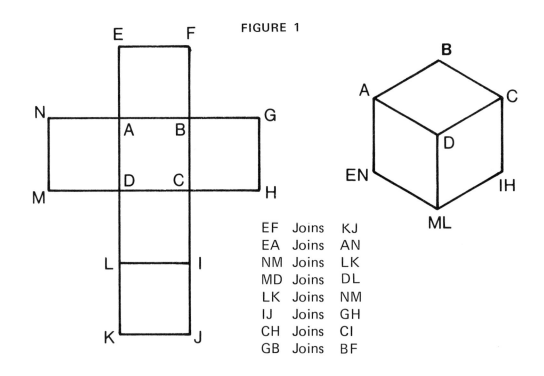

EF Joins KJ
EA Joins AN
NM Joins LK
MD Joins DL
LK Joins NM
IJ Joins GH
CH Joins CI
GB Joins BF

1.

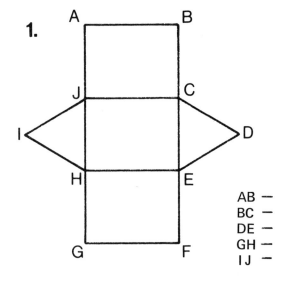

AB —
BC —
DE —
GH —
IJ —

2.

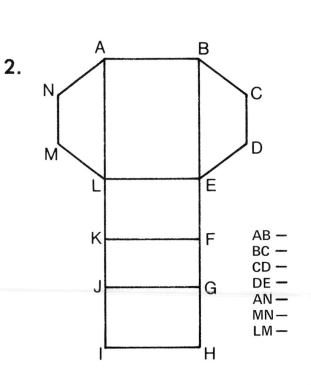

AB —
BC —
CD —
DE —
AN —
MN —
LM —

38

3.

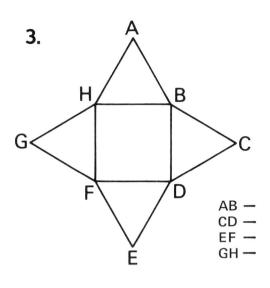

AB —
CD —
EF —
GH —

4.

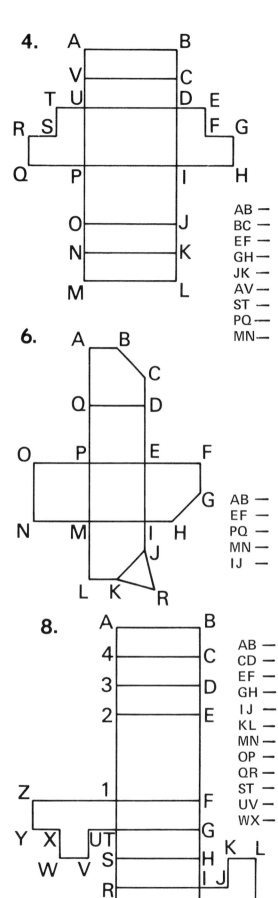

AB —
BC —
EF —
GH —
JK —
AV —
ST —
PQ —
MN—

5.

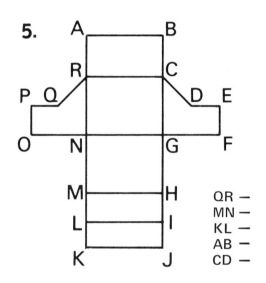

QR —
MN —
KL —
AB —
CD —

6.

AB —
EF —
PQ —
MN —
IJ —

7.

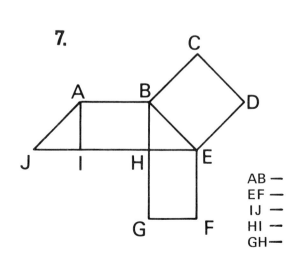

AB —
EF —
IJ —
HI —
GH—

8.

AB —
CD —
EF —
GH —
IJ —
KL —
MN —
OP —
QR —
ST —
UV —
WX —

EXERCISE 2-J

There are two parts to this section. In the first part there are five figures with numbers and marks along their edges. The object is to imagine each of these cut into two parts by one straight line such that these two parts can be joined to form the rectangle shown above the figures. Indicate the arrangement by listing the two numbers in each figure that will be joined. The instructions for the second part are identical except that the figure to be made is an equilateral triangle.

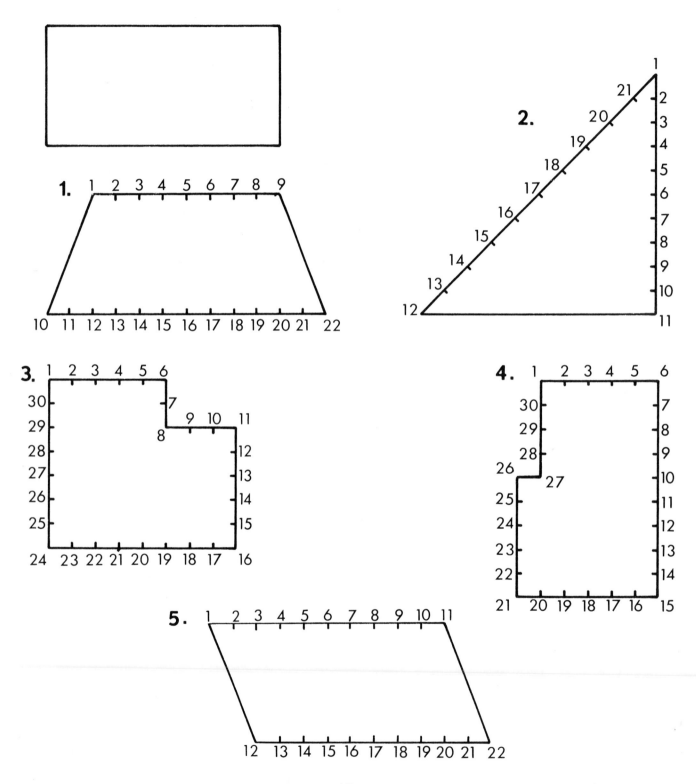

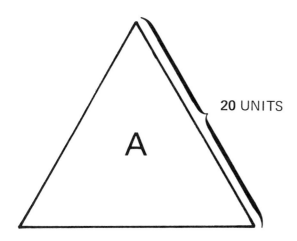

20 UNITS

A

6.

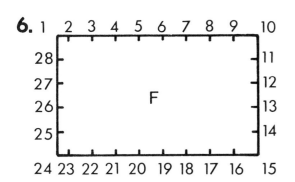

1 2 3 4 5 6 7 8 9 10
28 11
27 12
F
26 13
25 14
24 23 22 21 20 19 18 17 16 15

7.

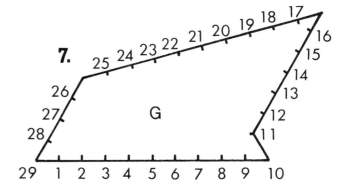

17
18
19 16
20 15
21 14
22 13
23
24 12
25 11
26
G
27
28
29 1 2 3 4 5 6 7 8 9 10

8.

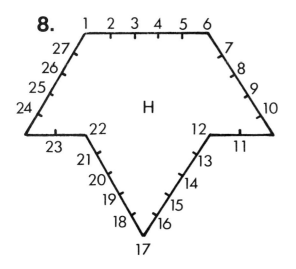

1 2 3 4 5 6
27 7
26 8
25 9
24 10
H
22 12
23 11
21 13
20 14
19 15
18 16
17

9.

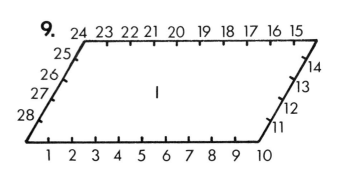

24 23 22 21 20 19 18 17 16 15
25
26 14
27 13
I
28 12
11
1 2 3 4 5 6 7 8 9 10

EXERCISE 2-K

The object in these exercises is to cut a rectangle into a specific number of identical parts in as many ways as possible. The cutting must be done along the grid lines on the rectangle, and the entire rectangle must be used. Figure 1 shows an example of the two ways a 2 x 3 rectangle can be cut into 3 congruent parts.

Divide these rectangles into the following numbers of congruent parts. Think of as many ways as possible for each number.

FIGURE 1

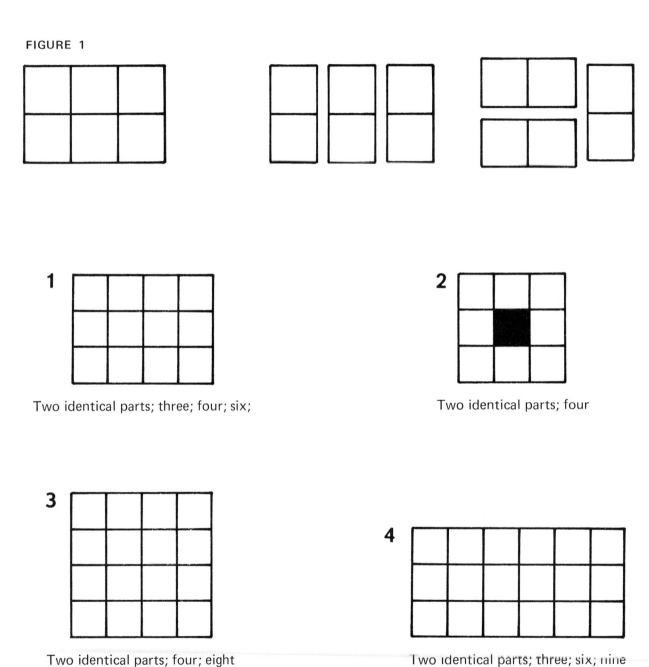

1   Two identical parts; three; four; six;

2   Two identical parts; four

3   Two identical parts; four; eight

4   Two identical parts; three; six; nine

PART III

CELL PATTERNS (TESSELLATIONS)

EXERCISE 3-A

The pattern in Figure 1 is made up of 16 squares. Four of the squares are black, four are white and eight are half black and half white. Each square can be thought of as a cell and the entire array as a 16 cell pattern.

The following patterns are made from either 4, 9 or 16 of the cells from the 16 cell pattern in Figure 1. Try to identify the individual cells that make up these patterns.

Figure 1

4 CELL PATTERNS

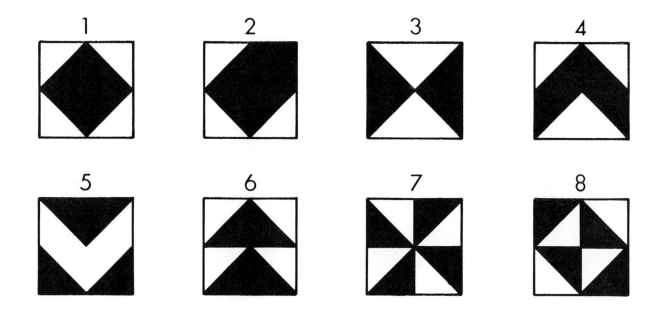

9 CELL PATTERNS

16 CELL PATTERNS

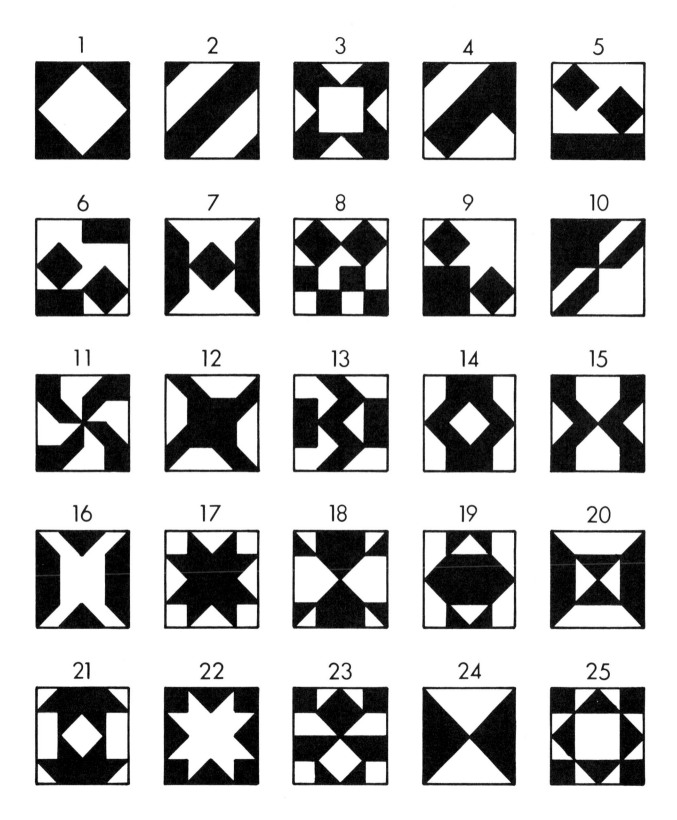

EXERCISE 3-B

The pattern in Figure 1 is made up of 18 equilateral triangles. Six of the triangles are white, six are black and six have one black corner which makes them ¼ black and ¾ white.

The following patterns are made from 18 or less of the triangles described above. Try to identify the individual triangles that make up each pattern.

FIGURE 1

hollow

PART IV

ESTIMATIONS

EXERCISE 4-A

In this exercise you are to estimate the length of each line shown below. Give your answers to the nearest ¼ inch. You can consider your estimate correct if you are within ¼ inch of the actual length.

1 _____

2 _____

3 _____

4 _____

5 _____

6 _____

7 _____

8 _____

9 _____

10 _____

11 _____

12 _____

13 _____

14 _____

15 _____

16 _____

17 _____

18 _____

As an additional exercise, you may estimate the length of each line to the nearest centimeter.

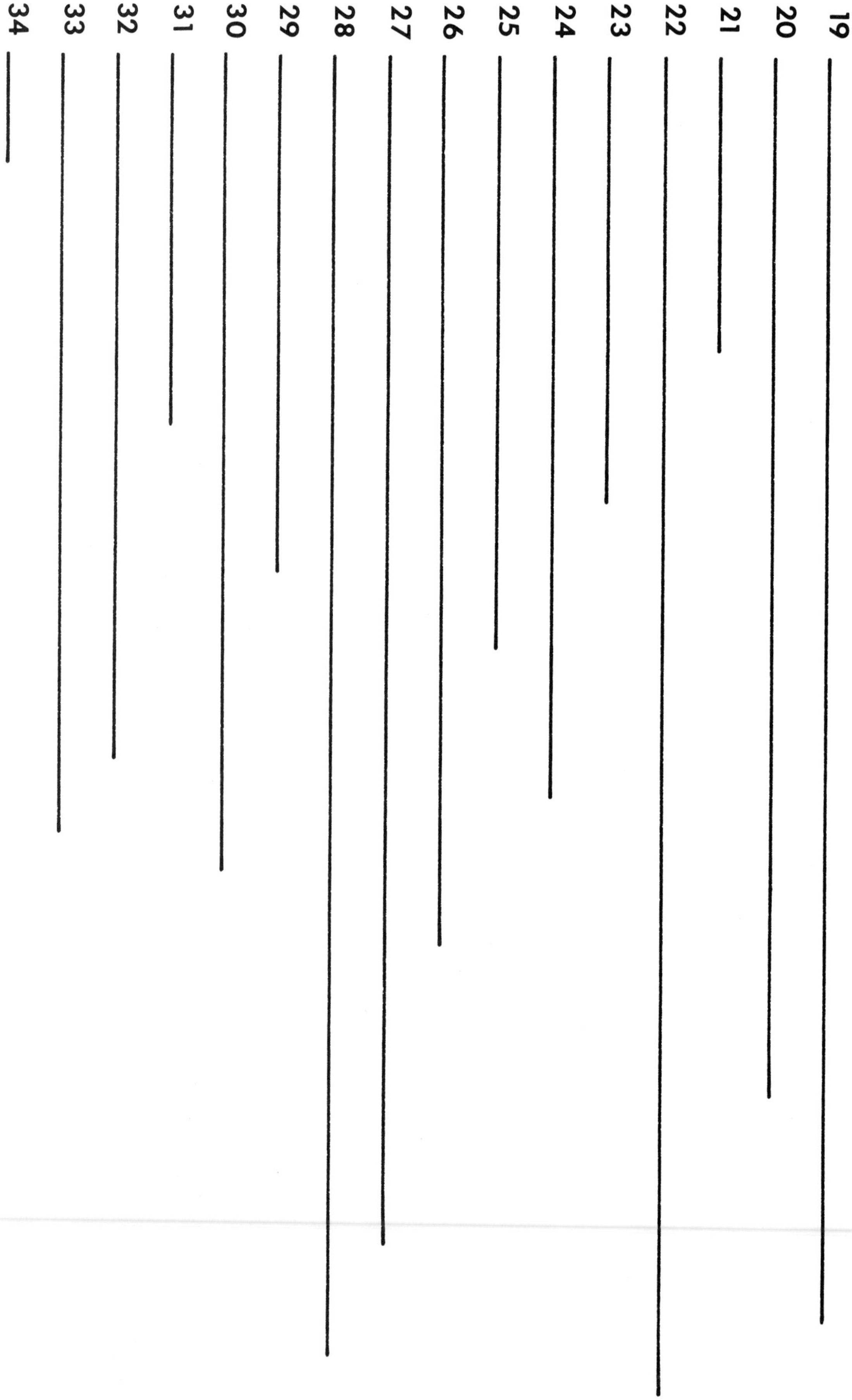

19

20

21

22

23

24

25

26

27

28

29

30

31

32

33

34

EXERCISE 4-B

Estimate the angle between the rays drawn below. If your answer is within 5 degrees of the actual angle, you can consider it correct. Figure 1 gives some angles to help you with your estimations.

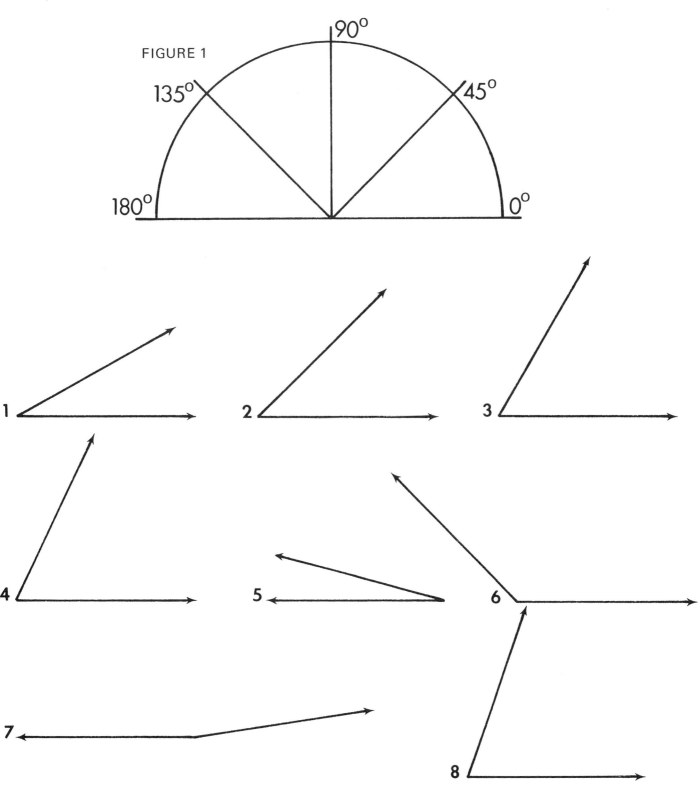

FIGURE 1

EXERCISE 4-C

Estimate the diameter of each of the circles below (don't measure them). List the letter designation of the circles in order from largest to smallest.

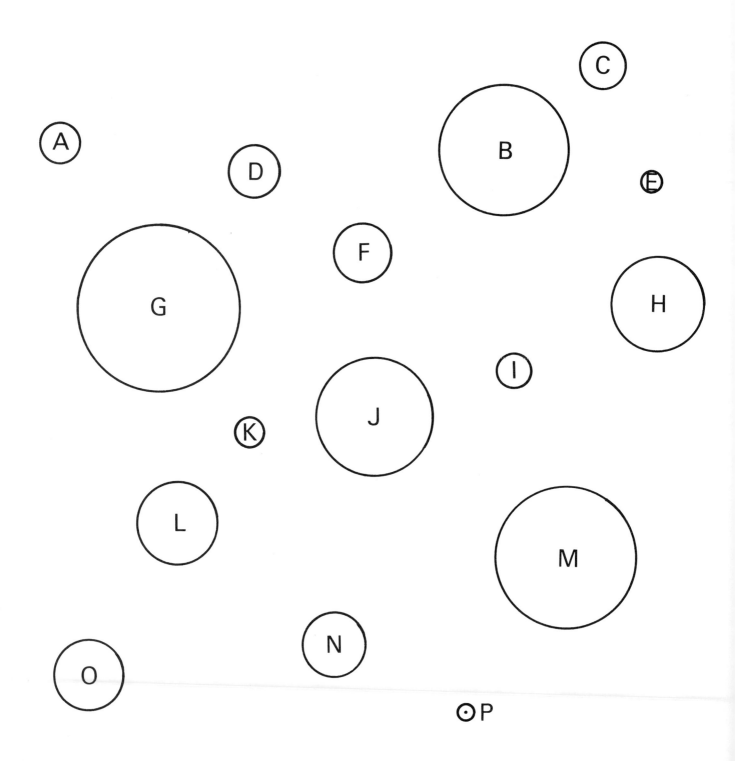

EXERCISE 4-D

Estimate what percent of each of the rectangles below is shaded and select the appropriate answer from the four given with each figure.

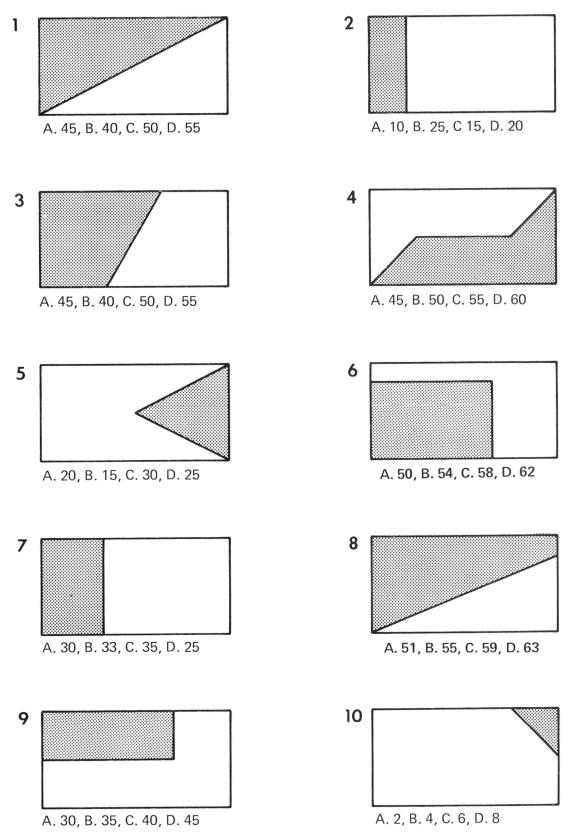

1

A. 45, B. 40, C. 50, D. 55

2

A. 10, B. 25, C 15, D. 20

3

A. 45, B. 40, C. 50, D. 55

4

A. 45, B. 50, C. 55, D. 60

5

A. 20, B. 15, C. 30, D. 25

6

A. 50, B. 54, C. 58, D. 62

7

A. 30, B. 33, C. 35, D. 25

8

A. 51, B. 55, C. 59, D. 63

9

A. 30, B. 35, C. 40, D. 45

10

A. 2, B. 4, C. 6, D. 8

EXERCISE 4-E

The shapes below are separated into various regions. Estimate the percentage of the total area of the shape each region occupies. It may be helpful to first think in terms of fractions and then convert to percents.

1

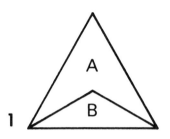

2

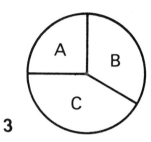

3

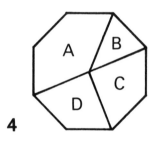

4

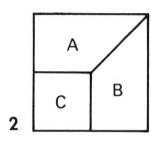

5

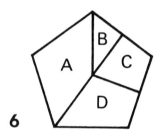

6

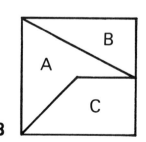

7

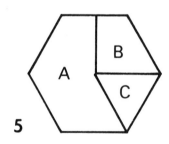

8

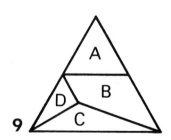

9

PART V

EXERCISE—5A

Codes can be made using geometric configurations. Several are shown below. The first uses a square grid pattern something like a tic tac toe pattern with dots. The second and third are based on other arrangements of intersecting lines and dots. The fourth code is based on a hexagon and dots. The letter corresponds to the missing side as is shown in the sample. The fifth code is based on sets of parallel lines all perpendicular to a common line.

When you think you understand the codes, try decoding the messages given below each one.

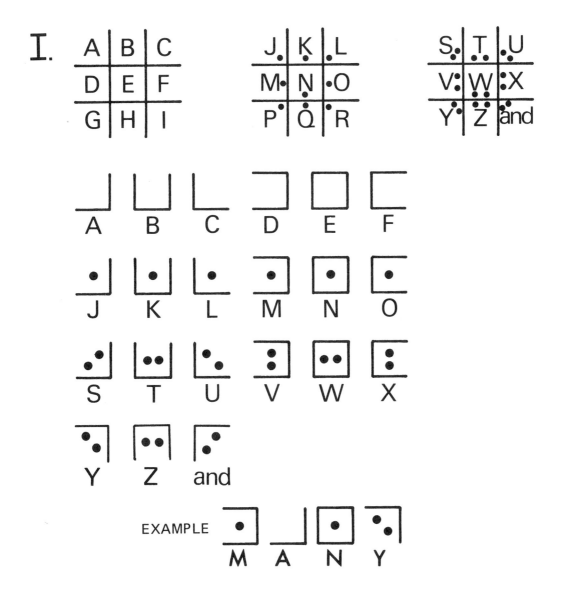

1. DECODE THIS MESSAGE

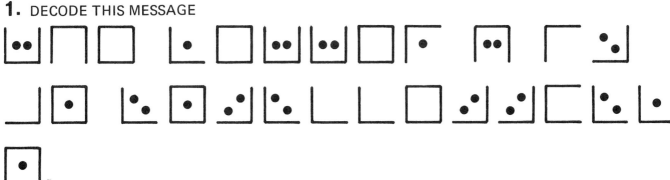

II.

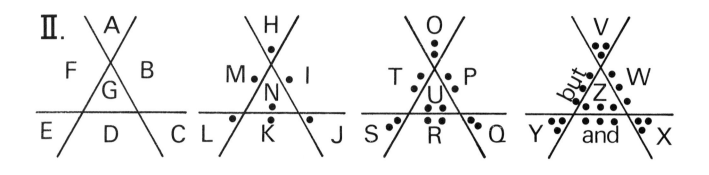

A B C D E F G H I J K L M N

O P Q R S T U V W X and Y but Z

EXAMPLE

E A S Y

DECODE THESE MESSAGES

2.

3.

III.

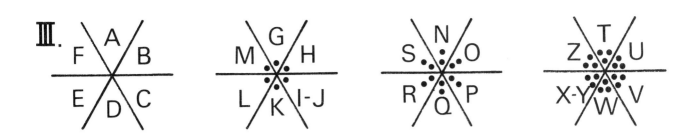

A   I   M   P   Z

EXAMPLE

F   U   N   N   Y

DECODE THIS MESSAGE

4.

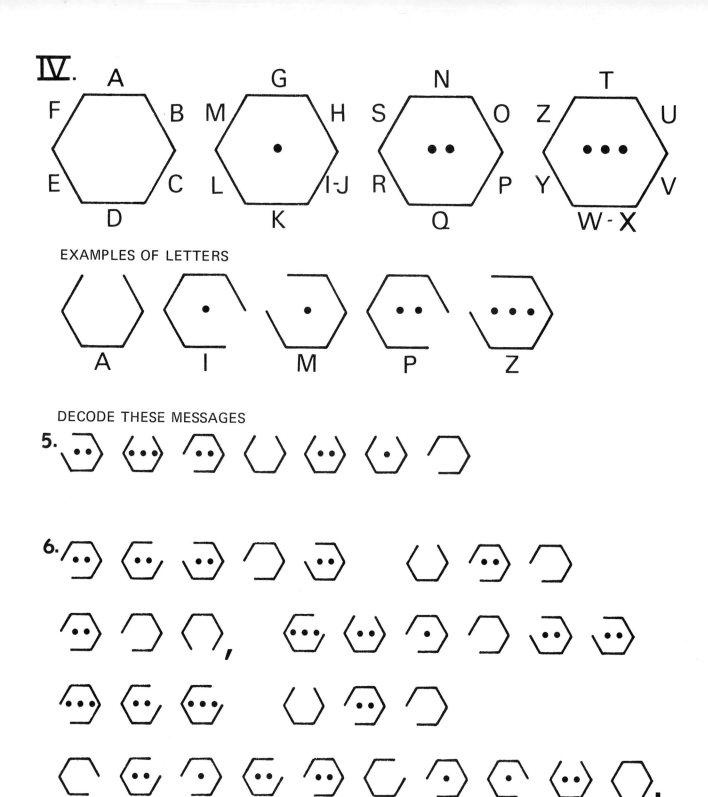

IV.

EXAMPLES OF LETTERS

DECODE THESE MESSAGES

5.

6.

Ⅴ.

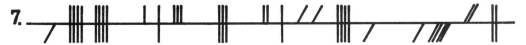

B C D F G A E I O U H J K L M

N P Q R S T V W X-Y Z

EXAMPLE

N U M B E R

DECODE THIS MESSAGE

7.

....AND THIS

8.

PART VI

MIRROR IMAGES AND REFLECTIONS

EXERCISE 6-A

Imagine two mirrors set up as shown in Figure 1. As you can see they reflect a letter placed between them three times. The challenge of this exercise is to fill in the three reflections of each of the letters below. The letter A has already been done as an example.

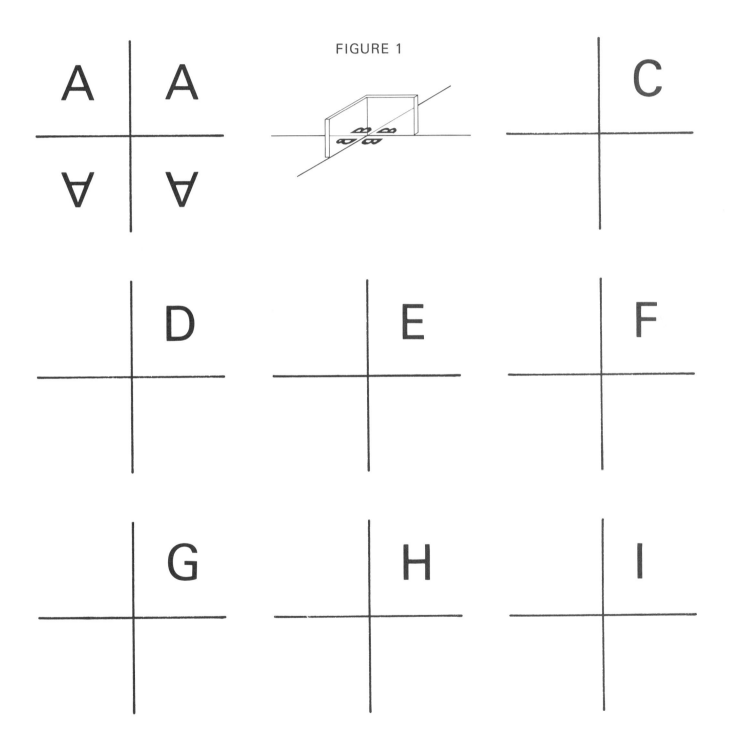

FIGURE 1

J   K   L

M   N   O

P   Q   R

S   T   U

V	W	X

Y	Z	a

e	g	t

3	4	6

The object of this exercise is to draw the mirror image of the word given below the line directly above it or vice versa. This has been done with the word, DECORATION as an example.

DECORⱯꓕIOИ
_____
DECORATION   SASSAFRASS
∩
_____   _____   _____
JANUARY   FEBRUARY   MARCH

_____   _____   _____   _____
NORTH   SOUTH   EAST   WEST
APRIL MAY JUNE
_____   _____   _____
JULY August

!
_____
A stitch in time saves nine.

_____
MAKE   MINE   MUSIC
October
_____
September   Ꝓ   November
1235813
_____
DECEMBER   6389

66

Imagine two mirrors set up as shown in Figure 1. As is shown, they reflect a word placed between them, three times. The challenge of this exercise is to write in the words given in each figure as they would appear reflected in such a mirror arrangement. The word BOY is already done as an example.

FIGURE 1

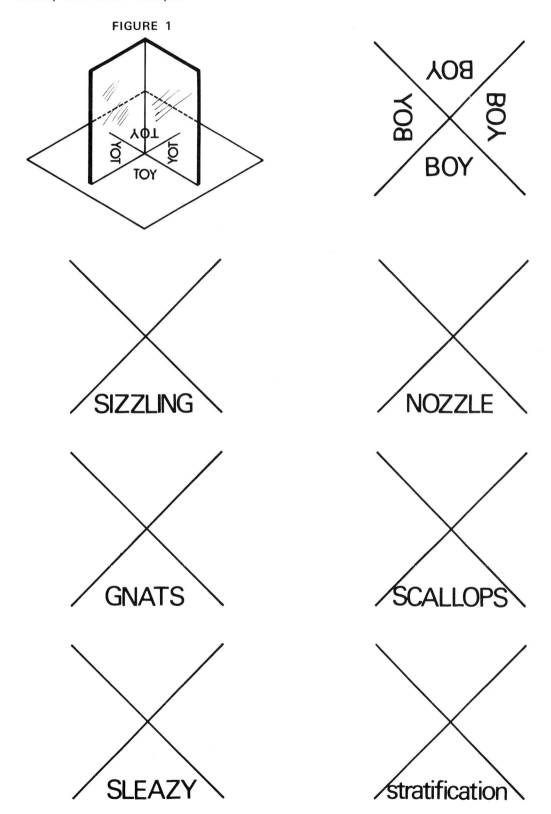

EXERCISE 6-D

Each of the "clock faces" below is a mirror image of the real clock. Can you tell what time the real clock shows in each case?

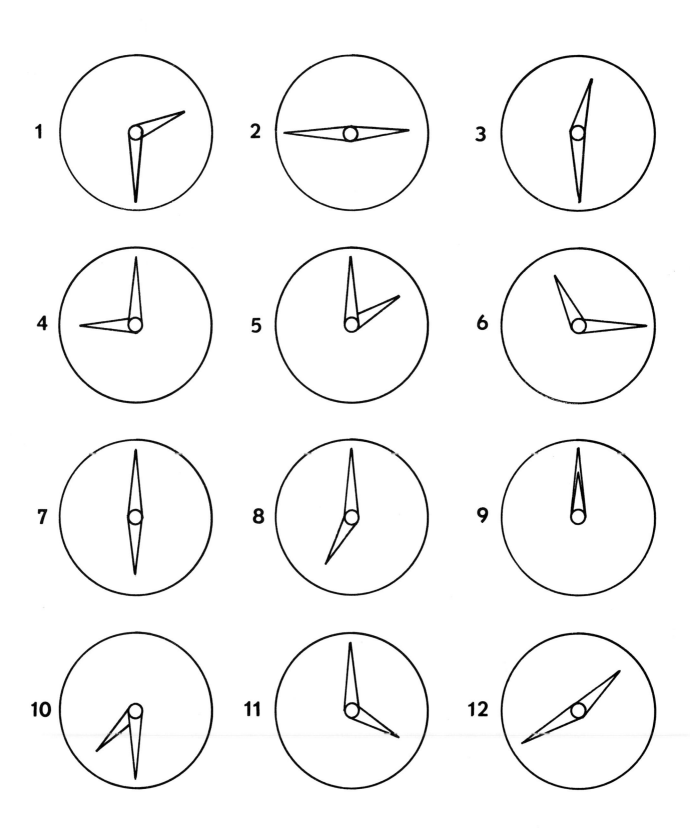

Can you read what it says below without looking in a mirror?

Asked what changes we could expect by the year 2000, a scientist pondered a minute, then replied, "Well, Brigitte Bardot will be 65."

A suburbanite told his neighbor: "I'm thinking of becoming a bigamist. There's too much grass in this yard for one wife to cut."

Nature had a sense of humor to let houndsecleaning, gardening, and spring fever come at the same time.

"I sure wish you'd let me take my bath in the morning instead of at night," my first-grade child said to me one evening. "Our teacher always asks us in Health whether or not we had a bath today, and I haven't been able to say 'yes' all year."

A civilized country is one where a person must go to a backward area in order to breathe pure, clean air.

Five homes can be built from the wood of a single 300-foot-tall West Coast redwood tree. Unfortunately, one redwood tree cannot be built from the wood of five homes.

At the ballpark I sat next to a real baseball fanatic. Without hesitation he could rattle off batting averages home runs and runs-batted-in for every player. I was amazed. Praising him for his memory, I asked, "Do you ever forget your wedding anniversary?" "Never!," he answered. "I was married the day Bobby Thomson hit the home run that won the pennant for the Giants. I'll never forget that day."

PART VII

PLANES, REGIONS, POINTS AND LINES

EXERCISE 7-A

A popular puzzle uses a diagram like that below. The problem is to draw three lines in such a manner that each of the seven dots is enclosed all by itself. There are many solutions. One solution is shown.

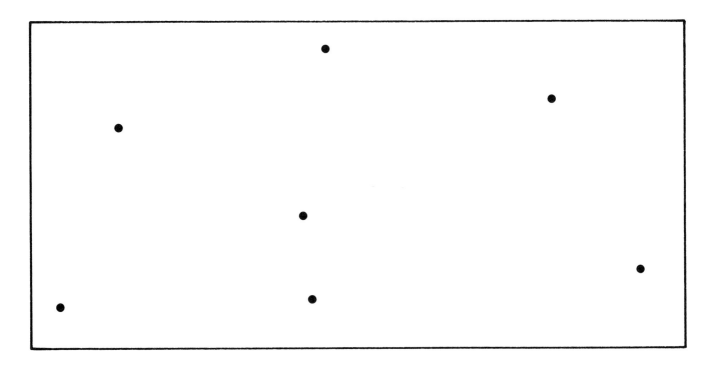

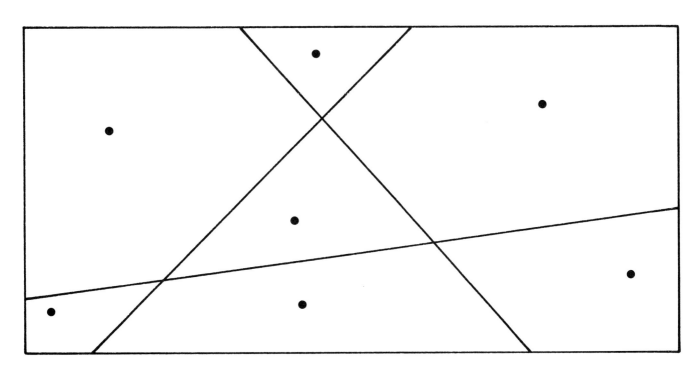

Exercises like this are not all easy. It would have been easier to start with the lines and then mark the points. In the drawing below, seven lines divide the rectangle into 29 regions.

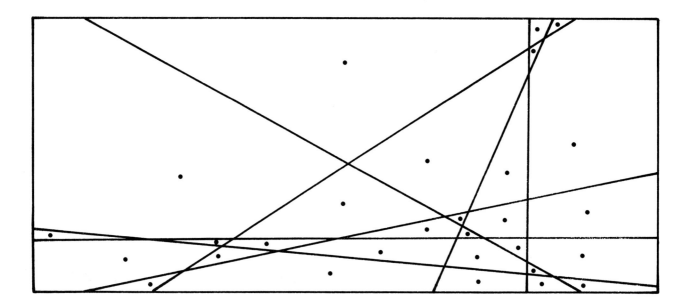

The pattern which governs the region/point/line problem is very interesting. When you have a sheet of paper without lines, you have one region. A single line separates the paper into two regions. Two lines separate the paper into four regions.

Examine the table below; it compares the number of lines and the regions.

Lines	Regions
0	1
1	2
2	4
3	7
4	11
5	16
6	22
7	29

Follow the slanted lines. They will tell you how to guess the next number of regions. What is your guess?

If you have had some algebra, you will recognize that the formula which predicts the *maximum* number of regions is $\underline{\frac{L(L+1)}{2} + 1}$.

2

In the previous exercise we attempted to predict the *maximum* number of regions. It can be fun to try some exercises that don't necessarily yield the *greatest* number of regions.

For example:

1. Draw two lines across a sheet of paper to produce only 3 regions.
2. Draw three lines across a sheet of paper to produce only 4 regions.
3. Draw three lines to produce only 6 regions.

In the following exercises you must use only straight lines. These can intersect or be parallel. One line *cannot* lie on top of another line, that is, the lines must be *distinct*. When you are instructed to use five lines, you must be able to see all 5 different lines (or segments of lines).

1. See whether or not you can find more than one way to do one of these space exercises.

Number of Lines	Number of Regions Required
1	2
2	3 4
3	4 5 6 7
4	5 6 7 8 9 10 11
5	6 7 8 9 10 11 12 13 14 15 16

2.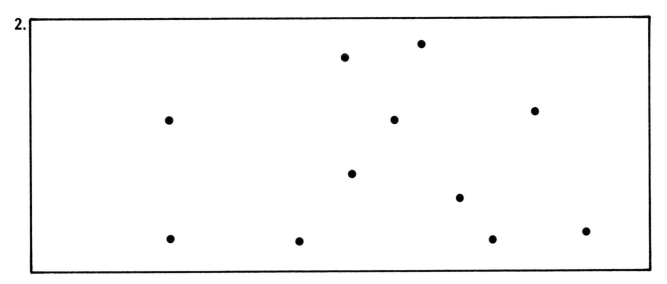

A. Can you isolate the eleven points above with exactly four lines?

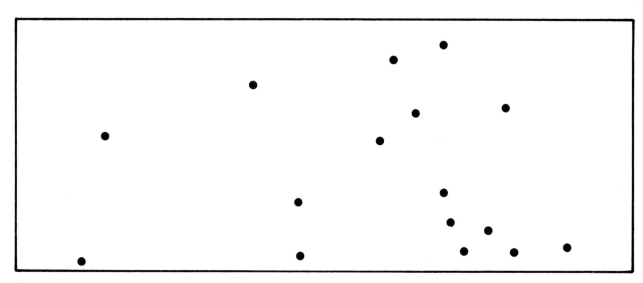

B. Can you isolate the sixteen points above with exactly five lines?

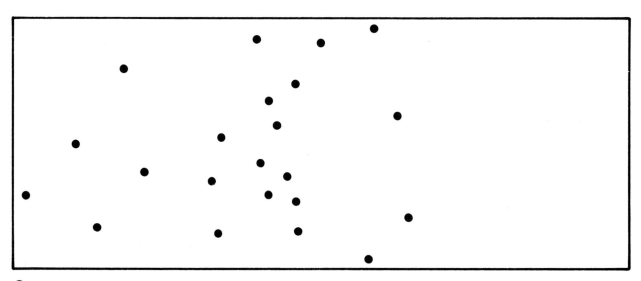

C. Can you isolate the twenty-two points above with exactly six lines?

In each of the 9 groups of figures in this exercise a figure is circled. The object of the exercise is to circle all the other figures in that group that contain the circled figure. For example, in the first group the circled figure is found in Figure A. Note that the figure may be in more than one drawing and that it must appear in exactly the same position in each case.

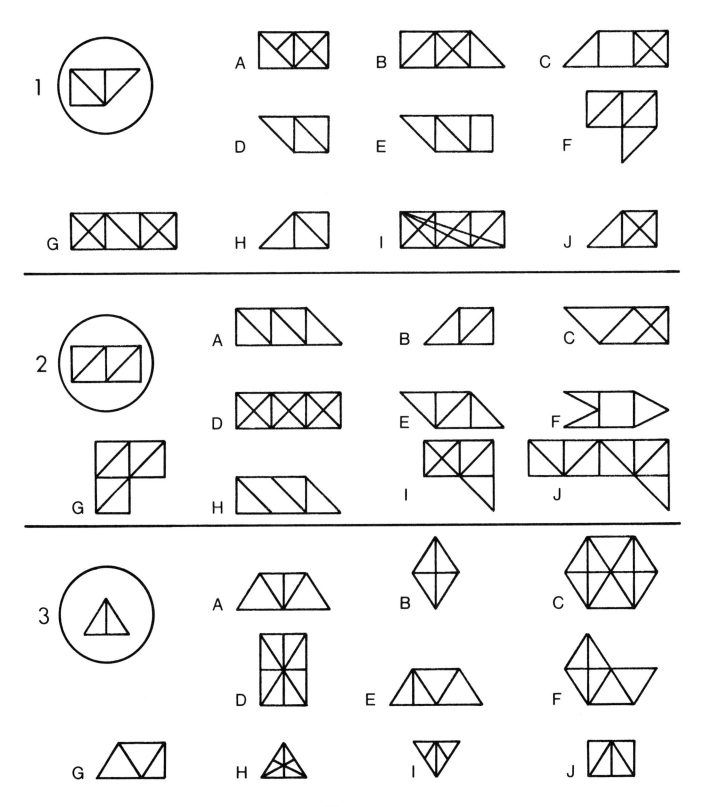

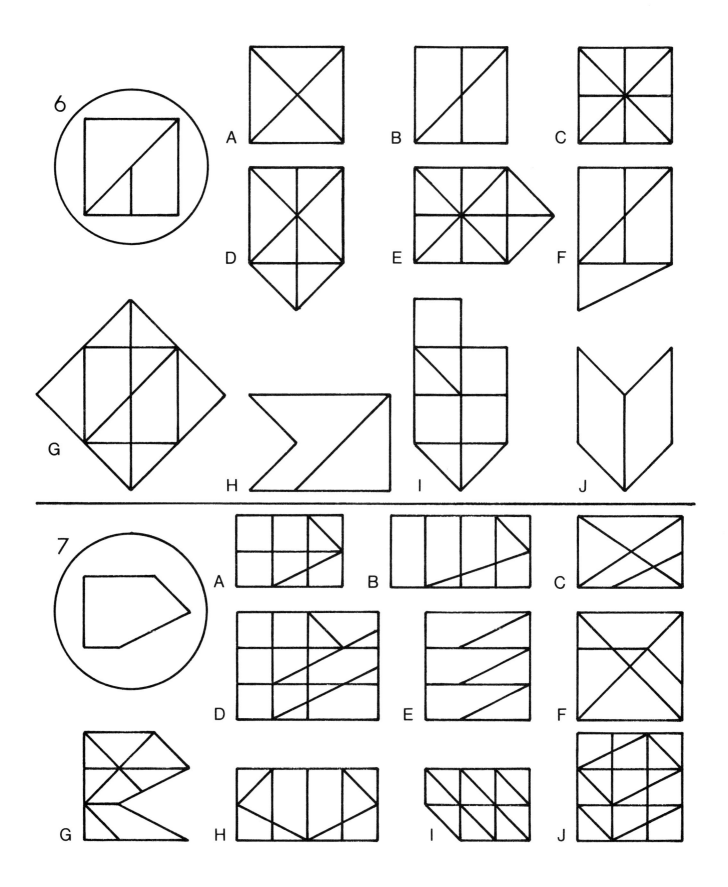

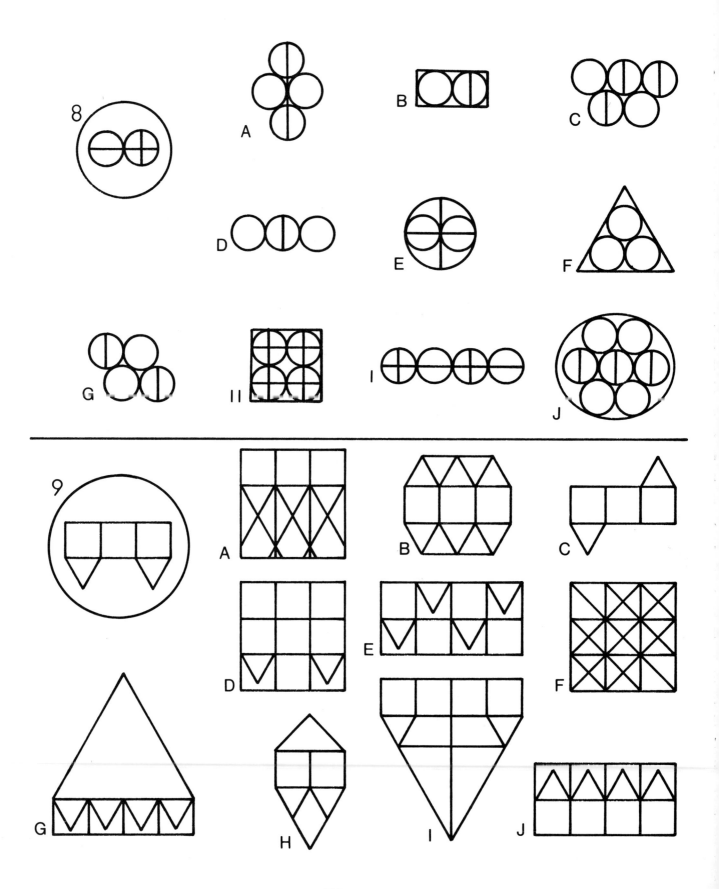

8

A

B

C

D

E

F

G

H

I

J

9

A

B

C

D

E

F

G

H

I

J

78

EXERCISE 7-C

When two or more lines pass through a common point, they are said to be *concurrent*. Imagine the lines in the sets below extended and select those that are concurrent. For example, lines 1, 2, 3 in Figure 1 are concurrent because they do pass through a common point.

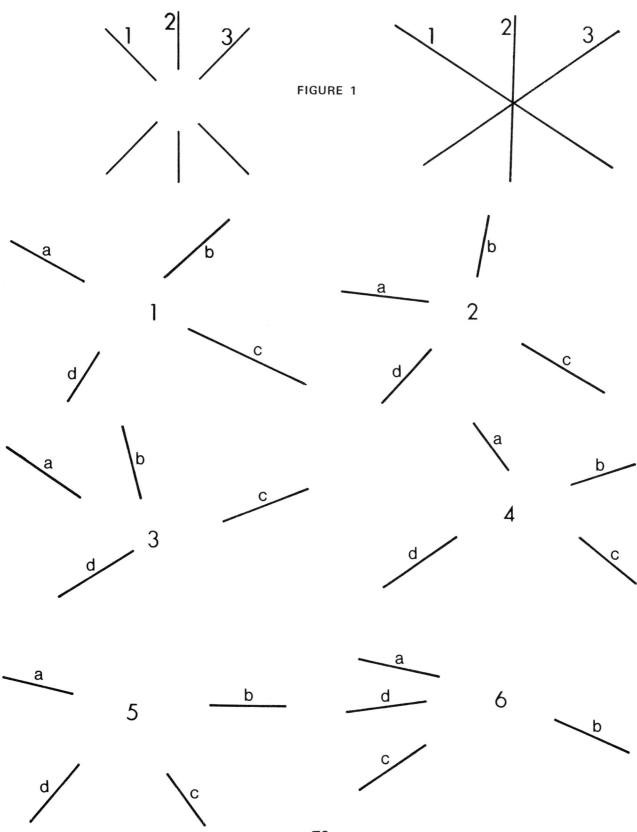

FIGURE 1

EXERCISE 7-D

In the figures below four parallel lines enter from one side of a rectangle. Only one emerges from the other side. You are to select which one it is without using a straight edge.

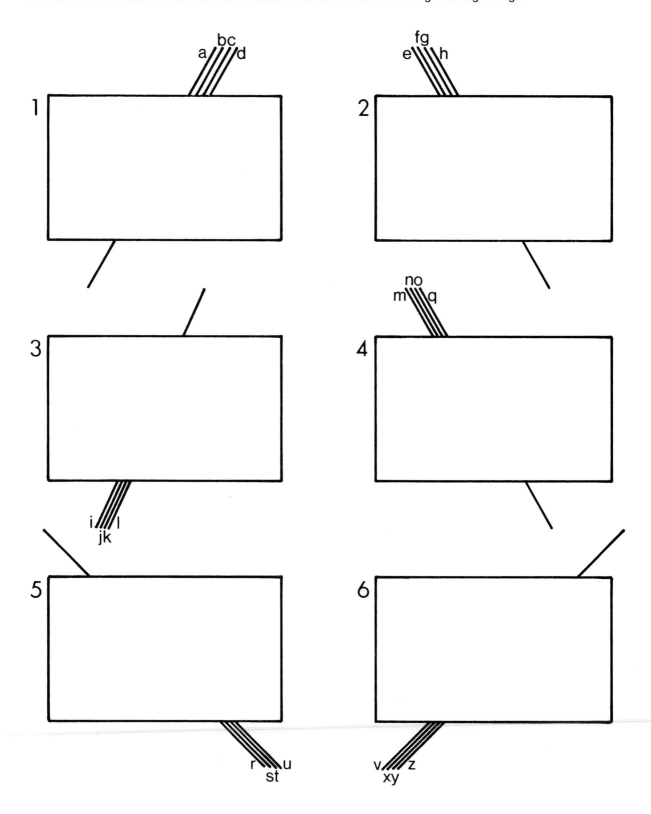

MISCELLANEOUS EXERCISES

EXERCISE 8-A

Can you read the incomplete words written below? They are printed in a type that resembles handwriting and the center half has been removed. Psychologists call the ability to complete incomplete images *closure*.

EXERCISE 8-B (Pencil Golf)

Two contestants help in laying out a golf course, drawing it on a large sheet of paper. You can make as many holes or as few as you like. The course can have lakes, sandtraps, trees and all sorts of hazards. Decide on a penalty to be connected with each hazard. You keep score just as in a real golf game.

The first player starts with the tip of his pencil inside the first tee. He closes his eyes and tries to draw a line to Hole 1. He then opens his eyes, sees where he is, and takes a second shot. When he manages to get the tip of the pencil inside Hole 1, the second player takes over. When either player lands in one of the hazards, he takes the penalty, closes his eyes, and takes another "stroke."

Figures 1 and 2 are examples of play. On Hole 1 the player went right over the trap. The second stroke landed him inside the cup. On Hole 2 the player shot over the first trap, but landed inside the second trap. He had a penalty of one stroke. His next shot landed inside the cup. His score for this hole was 3 because he took two shots plus a penalty stroke.

You can develop a complete golf course and use it over and over. The game can also be played at the chalkboard.

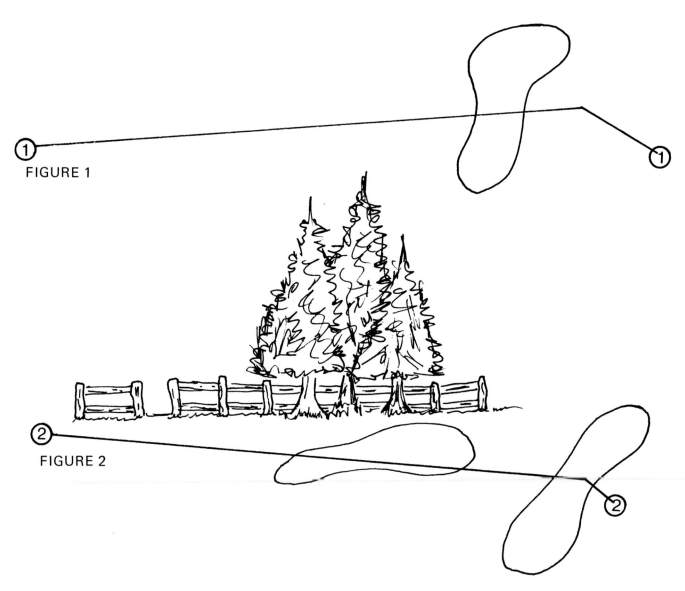

FIGURE 1

FIGURE 2

Select the pairs or sets of three like figures from those below.

EXERCISE 8-D

There are 44 pairs of figures below and two that don't have mates. Find these two.

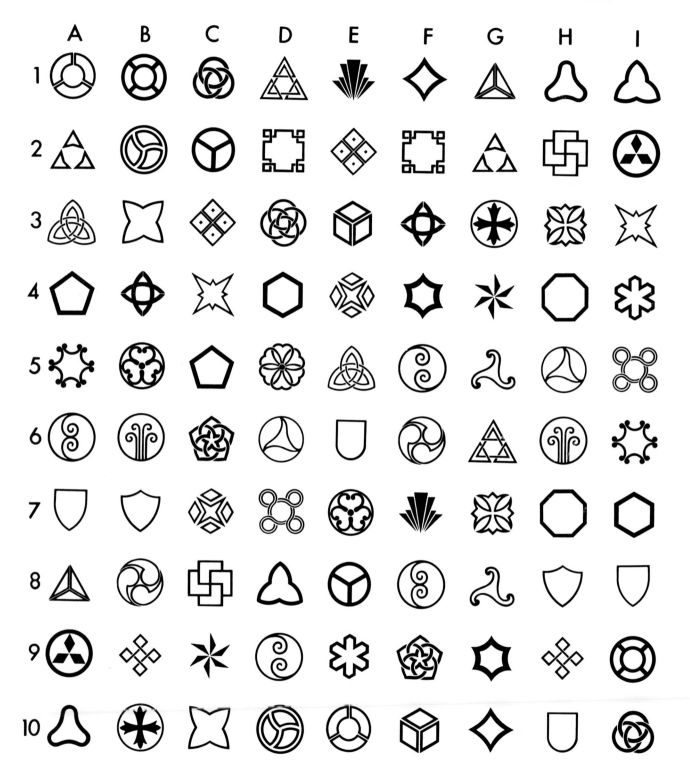

EXERCISE 8-E

The object of this exercise is to count the number of cubes in each of the stacks below. Assume that the blocks are resting on the others when more than one layer is involved.

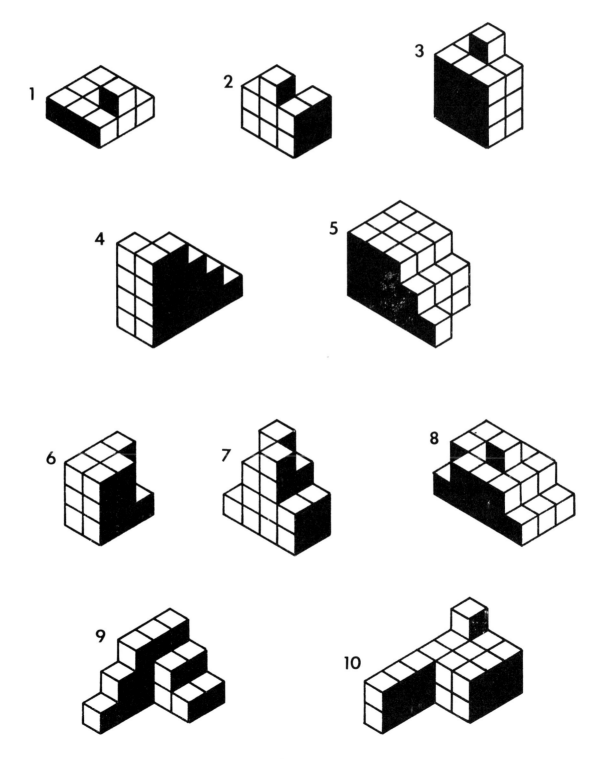

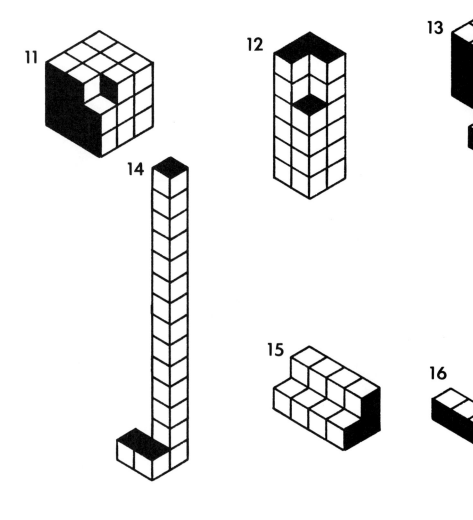

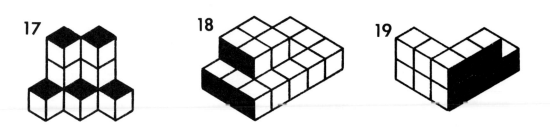

EXERCISE 8-F (Bulls Eye)

This game is excellent for developing control in drawing. You begin with a drawing like Figure 1 . It consists of 16 dots; the home dot is marked X. The others are labeled 1 to 15. Two people play the game. Toss a coin to determine which player goes first.

Here is an example of the game. Suppose Al wins the toss. Bill, the other player, decides all of Al's moves. He might tell Al to go from X to 12. Al must make a line which goes from X to 12. Bill then calls another course that starts at 12 and goes to any uncircled number—say from 12 to 2. Al connects the 12 to the 2, circling the 2. The game continues until Bill gets Al back to the Home dot (X). If Al touches any number or any bull's eye or any path, he stops. His score is the number of dots he has connected without errors. Then Bill gets a turn to play with Al calling out directions. The winner is the player to connect the most dots without errors.

The trick is to give yourself plenty of room. Figure 2 is a typical solution in the order: X, 12, 2, 7, 13, 15, 9, 4, 1, 6, 8, 10, 5. The game ends at 5. The player had to give up when directed to go from 5 to 3. He had not left enough room to thread his way through the "maze" of lines to 3. His score was 13.

FIGURE 1

X	1	2	3
4	5	6	7
8	9	10	11
12	13	14	15

FIGURE 2

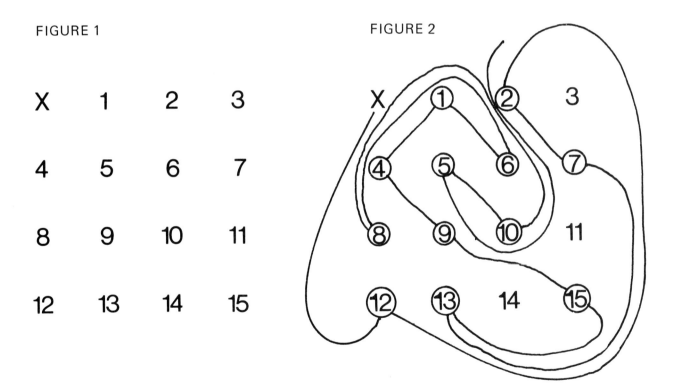

SOLUTIONS

Exercise 1-A Page 11

1-C	6-A	11-D
2-D	7-B	12-B
3-C	8-D	13-A
4-C	9-D	14-D
5-B	10-D	

Exercise 1-B Page 14

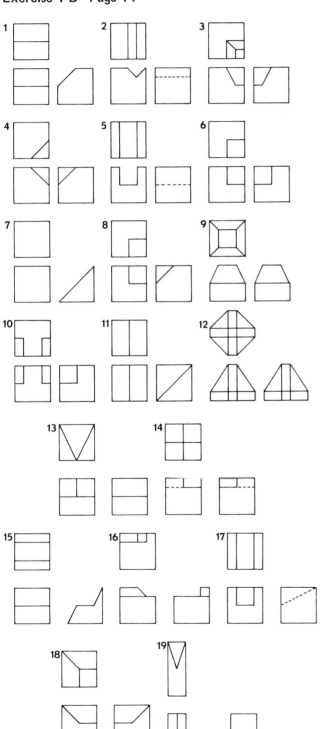

Exercise 1-C Page 16

Exercise 2-A Page 19

1-A	5-D
2-D	6-B
3-D	7-D
4-D	

Exercise 2-B Page 21

1-C	3-B
2-C	4-C

Exercise 2-C Page 22

1-C	3-D
2-A	4-B

Exercise 2-D Page 23

1-I	8-B	15-S
2-C	9-G	16-N
3-J	10-E	17-K
4-H	11-M	18-P
5-F	12-R	19-L
6-D	13-T	20-Q
7-A	14-O	

Exercise 2-E Page 27

1-1	4-4
2-2	5-2
3-1	6-

SOLUTIONS

Exercise 2-F   Page 29

1-H	5-C	9-I
2-L	6-F	10-K
3-A	7-B	11-E
4-J	8-G	12-D

Exercise 2-G   Page 31

1-F	5-A	9-B
2-J	6-K	10-G
3-D	7-E	11-C
4-L	8-H	12-I

Exercise 2-H   Page 33

1-D	7-D	13-B	19-C
2-A	8-A	14-A	20-C
3-B	9-D	15-C	21-B
4-C	10-C	16-B	22-D
5-B	11-B	17-D	23-A
6-B	12-A	18-A	24-C

Exercise 2-I   Page 38

1. AB-GF
   BC-DC
   DE-FE
   GH-IH
   IJ-AJ

2. AB-IH
   BC-HG
   CD-GF
   DE-FE
   AN-IJ
   MN-KJ
   LM-LK

3. AB-CB
   CD-ED
   EF-GF
   GH-AH

4. AB-ML
   BC-FE
   EF-CB
   GH-KJ
   JK-HG
   AV-ST
   ST-AV
   PQ-PO
   MN-SR

5. QR-AR
   MN-ON
   KL-QP
   AB-KJ
   CD-CB

6. AB-LK
   EF-ED
   PQ-PO
   MN-ML
   IJ-IH

7. AB-CB
   EF-ED
   IJ-GF
   HI-HG
   GH-IH

8. AB-QP
   CD-ON
   EF-ML
   GH-KJ
   IJ-IH
   KL-GF
   MN-ED
   OP-CB
   QR-WV
   ST-UT
   UV-SR
   WX-A4
   YZ-23
   YX-34
   1Z-12

Exercise 2-J   Page 40

1.	1-12 or 9-20	6.	1-15 or 24-10
2.	17-6	7.	11-21
3.	29-8	8.	12-22
4.	20-27	9.	10-19
5.	3-12 or 11-20		

Exercise 2-K   Page 42

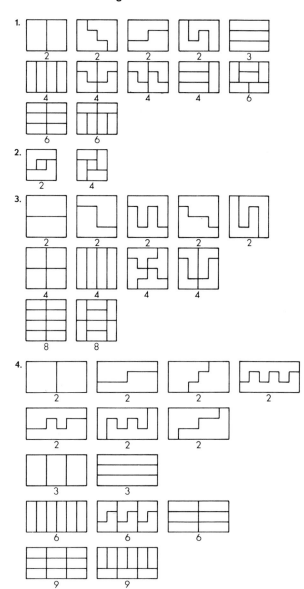

90

SOLUTIONS

Exercise 4-A   Page 51

	INCHES	CM			INCHES	CM
1.	6½	17	18.		1¼	3
2.	3½	9	19.		8½	22
3.	5½	14	20.		7	18
4.	2½	6	21.		2	5
5.	4½	12	22.		9	23
6.	1½	4	23.		3	8
7.	3	8	24.		5	13
8.	5	13	25.		4	10
9.	2	5	26.		6	15
10.	6	15	27.		8	21
11.	6¾	17	28.		8¾	22
12.	1	3	29.		3½	9
13.	5¼	13	30.		5½	14
14.	3¼	8	31.		2½	6
15.	6¼	16	32.		4¾	12
16.	4	10	33.		5¼	13
17.	3¾	10	34.		¾	2

Exercise 4-B   Page 53

1-30°	4-15°
2-45°	6-135°
3-60°	7-170°
4-65°	8-70°

Exercise 4-C   Page 54

G	H	F	I
M	L	D	K
B	O	C	E
J	N	A	P

Exercise 4-D   Page 55

1.	C(50%)	6.	B(54%)
2.	D(20%)	7.	B(33%)
3.	C(50%)	8.	C(59%)
4.	B(50%)	9.	B(35%)
5.	D(25%)	10.	D(8%)

Exercise 4-E   Page 56

1.	A(66⅔%)	6.	A(40%)
	B(33⅓%)		B(10%)
2.	A(37½%)		C(20%)
	B(37½%)		D(30%)
	C(25%)	7.	A(12½%)
3.	A(25%)		B(25%)
	B(30%)		C(17%)
	C(45%)		D(45½%)
4.	A(37½%)	8.	A(37½%)
	B(12½%)		B(25%)
	C(25%)		C(37½%)
	D(25%)	9.	A(25%)
5.	A(58⅓%)		B(37½%)
	B(25%)		C(25%)
	C(16⅔%)		D(12½%)

Exercise 5-A   Page 57

1. The letter Z is an unsuccessful N.
2. Candy tastes dandy.
3. It is snowing. Hail the snow!
4. Happy birthday wherever you are.
5. Strange.
6. Roses are red, unless you are colorblind.
7. The end.

Exercise 6-A   Page 63

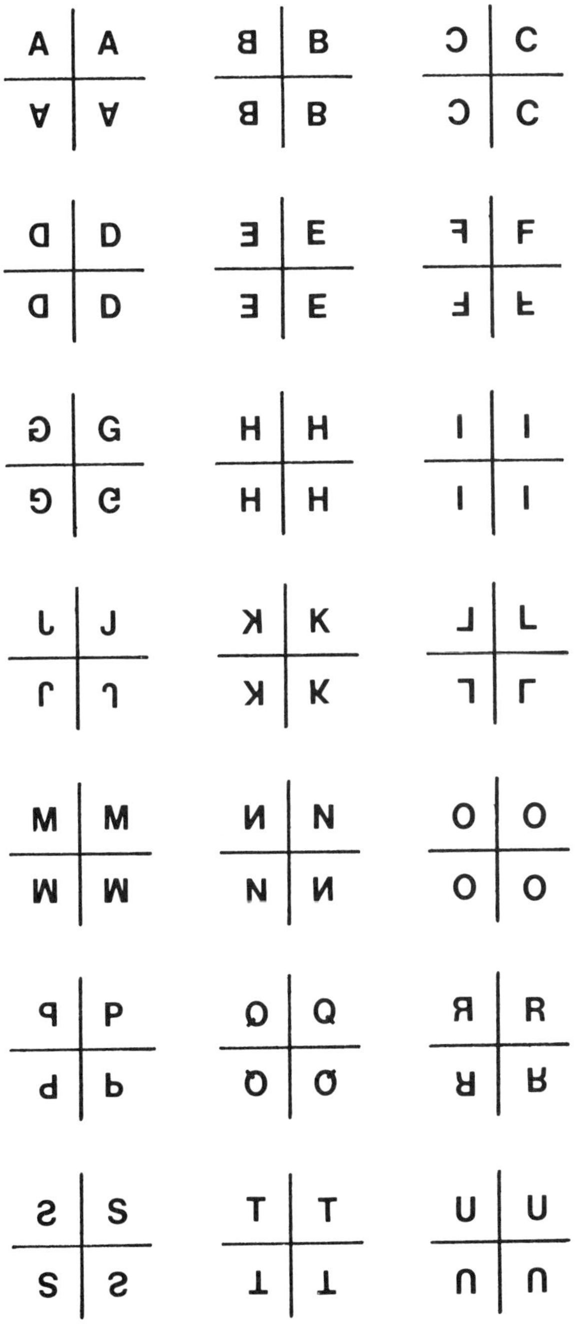

Exercise 6-A (cont.)

V	V		W	W		X	X
V	V		W	W		X	X

Y	Y		Z	Z		a	a
Y	Y		Z	Z		a	a

e	e		g	g		f	f
e	e		g	g		f	f

3	3		4	4		6	6
3	3		4	4		6	6

Exercise 6-B   Page 66

DECORATION   SASSAFRASS

JANUARY   FEBRUARY   MARCH

NORTH   SOUTH   EAST   WEST

APRIL   MAY   JUNE   JULY   August

A stitch in time saves nine.

MAKE   MINE   MUSIC

September   October   November

DECEMBER   6389123 58 13

Exercise 6-C   Page 67

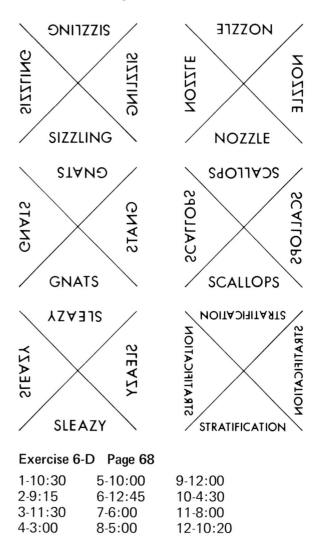

SIZZLING

NOZZLE

GNATS

SCALLOPS

SLEAZY

STRATIFICATION

Exercise 6-D   Page 68

1-10:30	5-10:00	9-12:00
2-9:15	6-12:45	10-4:30
3-11:30	7-6:00	11-8:00
4-3:00	8-5:00	12-10:20

Exercise 6-E   Page 69

Asked what changes we could expect by the year 2000, a scientist pondered a minute, then replied, "Well, Brigitte Bardot will be 65."

A suburbanite told his neighbor: "I'm thinking of becoming a bigamist. There's too much grass in this yard for one wife to cut."

Nature had a sense of humor to let housecleaning, gardening, and spring fever come at the same time.

"I sure wish you'd let me take my bath in the morning instead of night," my first-grade child said to me one evening. "Our teacher always asks us in Health whether or not we had a bath today, and I haven't been able to say "yes" all year."

A civilized country is one where a person must go to a backward area in order to breathe pure, clean air.

Five homes can be built from the wood of a single 300-foot-tall West Coast redwood tree. Unfortunately, one redwood tree cannot be built from the wood of five homes.

SOLUTIONS

Exercise 6-E (cont.)

At the ballpark I sat next to a real baseball fanatic. Without hesitation he could rattle off batting averages, home runs and runs-batted-in for every player. I was amazed. Praising him for his memory, I asked, "Do you ever forget your wedding anniversary?" "Never!", he answered. "I was married the day Bobby Thomson hit the home run that won the pennant for the Giants. I'll never forget that day."

Exercise 7-A   Page 71

Example

1

2

3

Problem 1

1   2

3

4

5

Exercise 7-A (cont.)

Problem 2

A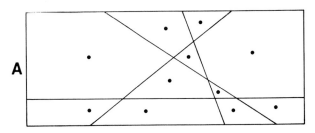

B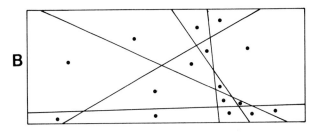

C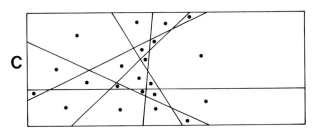

Exercise 7-B   Page 75

1. A,G,I
2. D,G,I
3. B,C,D,E,F,H,J
4. D,I,J
5. A,C,D,G,I
6. B,C,D,E,F,G
7. A,D,G,H,J
8. H,I
9. A,B,D,E

Exercise 7-C   Page 79

1. a,b,d
2. a,b,d
3. a,b,c
4. a,b,d
5. a,b,c
6. a,c,d

Exercise 7-D   Page 80

1-B   3-I   5-T
2-E   4-N   6-X

SOLUTIONS

Exercise 8-A   Page 81

Come	Marines
Linen	Greasy
Fortune	Circles
Marker	Rulers
Pattern	Contour
Designs	Stands
Kindness	Magazine
Nearer	Pebbles
Plasticity	Exactly
Horror	Blessings

Exercise 8-C   Page 83

1-A and 7-C	3-A and 3-D
1-B and 5-A and 7-D	3-C and 6-B
1-C and 4-A and 6-D	4-B and 5-D
1-D and 3-B	4-C and 5-B
2-A and 2-D	4-D and 7-B
2-B and 6-C	5-C and 6-A
2-C and 7-A	

Exercise 8-D   Page 84

3-D
5-D

Exercise 8-E   Page 85

1-10	6-16	11-26	16-11
2-9	7-20	12-22	17-9
3-19	8-27	13-20	18-19
4-18	9-18	14-16	19-11
5-34	10-25	15-12	